COLOR YOUR

Using the Power of Color and Light in Your Life

by Rita Robinson

Newcastle Publishing Co.
North Hollywood, California

Edited by Gina Misiroglu
Cover and interior design by Michele Lanci-Altomare

ISBN: 0-87877-189-1
A Newcastle Book
First printing 1994
10 9 8 7 6 5 4 3 2 1
Printed in the United States of America.

To Dean Allen

A friend to writers, and those who love to read.

ACKNOWLEDGMENTS

Many individuals have added to my knowledge about how light and color affect our lives. My grateful thanks to: Bem P. Allen; Grace Atwood; David Avery, M.D.; Anita Baroldi; Philip M. Becker, M.D.; Alan Paul Brauer, M.D.; Dana Brookins; Tom Budzynski; Donna Caltrider; Nicki Cohen; Madeleine Conklin; Tracy Covington; Steven Cox; Maurizio Corbetta, M.D.; Stanley Coren; Barbara Cunningham; Chuck Downey; Joel Edelman; Seymour Fisher, M.D.; Richard E. George, M.D.; Robert Green; Brian Harris; Robert Henkin, M.D.; Lynn Henriksen; Blain Herbert; Valorie Hood; Valorie Hunt; Thor Kaslof; Waud Kracke; Theda Lambert; Thomas Mack, M.D.; Franklin R. Manis; Jean Mathews; Keith Merriman; Marvine N. Miller; Jane Milstead; Lisa Mobius; Wendy Nakao; Chris Newman; German Nino-Murcia; Aileen Penn; Ven Dr. Havanpola Ratanasara; Howard Roffwarg, M.D.; Norman E. Rosenthal, M.D.; Martin Seligman, M.D.; David Siever; Eric Silverman; Bobbe Sommers; Howard and Dorothy Sun; Patricia Verlodt; Paula Wade; Carlton Wagner; Ruth B. Weg; Myron Wolbarsht, M.D.; Charles Wysocki; Mike and Nancy Zorick.

Special thanks to Julia Sherley-Price, Liphook Hampshire, England.

CONTENTS

"Light! Nature's resplendent robe:

without whose vesting beauty

all were wrapt in gloom."

—James Thomson, eighteenth century Scottish poet

INTRODUCTION

In the mountain community of Big Bear, California, where I live, we're often treated to rich, vibrant sunrises, and deep colorful sunsets. One evening driving home, I pulled off the road to view a particularly colorful sunset over the lake of undulating purples, pinks, deep reds, and intense oranges. The vibrant colors filled the sky with a streaked kaleidoscope of illuminated colors that changed from minute to minute. It is a tourist town, populated on weekends by visitors from the Los Angeles and Orange County areas. These tourists were lined up along the road en masse snapping pictures of this unusual sunset. One man was weeping as he stood silently viewing the beauty of the scene before him.

Color and light abound within and about the human mind and spirit as cyclically and rhythmically as the vast oceans of the world. Swirls of color and light continually and unceasingly seep into the very cells of the human body making it one of the most powerful, yet subtle, forces encountered throughout life.

Despite the technological world today, which often throws the natural rhythms of daily life askew, people are affected by color and light much the same way as their primitive ancestors. Humans observe and feel the gray-rose dawn, the dazzling sunlight hours, the red-orange haze of sunset, and, lastly, the darkness of night, often with little thought to the beauty and adventure they have witnessed. Occasionally, though, like the weeping man viewing the sunset, we are reminded of our humanness and our link to the earth in the face of overwhelming emotional splendor. Perhaps it touches a cord of long suppressed, ancient, even primeval memories lying dormant within the cells of our bodies.

Early man and woman followed the dictates of this changing color panorama, initially created by visible light rays from the electromagnetic spectrum. As night approached, the body automatically slowed down, preparing the person for sleep. At dawn the body readied for action.

Symbolically and metaphorically the changing orchestration of color continued on through the night—in dream time—as man and woman slumbered.

Modern men and women also respond to this palette of color, with the dark blue night sky representing peace and calm, and the bright yellow of day epitomizing activity. Humans, though, respond to all colors, whether viewing a canvas, smelling a rose, or watching a burning log. Color is there producing responses, even at a subconscious level.

John Dewey writes in *Art As Experience* that in doing ordinary things, like stoking a log in the fireplace, men and women experience art. . . . "The man who poked the sticks of burning wood would say he did it to make the fire burn better; but he is nonetheless fascinated by the colorful drama of change enacted before his eyes and imaginatively partakes in it. He does not remain a cold spectator."

None remain sterile in the dappled face of colors flowing about daily, even though we might wonder why a certain color brings about a particular mood or reaction. Scientists are answering some of these questions. They have long known about the penetrating force of infrared (used in radiation treatments) and ultraviolet light (responsible for such conditions as sunburn). But newer studies show that visible light, that which we see as color, also penetrates muscle and tissue. The blind react to light and color through their skin, partly because colors affect metabolic and glandular activity, according to some studies. Hence, people may not only "see red" through the eye, but through the body's tissues and organs.

Because of this new understanding of color, humans are able to alter their feelings, moods, personalities—even their health—through color. They can also use the gift of color in their surroundings, clothing, and in the mind's eye to enlighten, to energize, to calm and to lift themselves from the mundane. People can mentally or physically touch certain colors to bring love into their lives, meditate on others to help in healing, or warm to the glow of symbolically colored burning candles. It is not a supernatural, or occult experience because that which we hold in consciousness, or the mind's eye, can become reality.

Color is there in abundance for the asking, even under the worst conditions. Holocaust survivor Viktor E. Frankl, developer of the Third School of Viennese Psychiatry, or logotherapy, writes in *Man's Search for Meaning* of his experiences and understanding achieved from his imprisonment. Throughout his experience, color is ever present. "Standing outside we saw sinister clouds glowing in the west and the whole sky alive with clouds of ever-changing shapes and colors, from steel blue to blood red. The desolate grey mud huts provided a sharp contrast, while the puddles on the muddy ground reflected the glowing sky. Then, after minutes of moving silence, one prisoner said to another, 'How beautiful the world could be!' "

The person Frankl was quoting wasn't simply "seeing" the beauty about him through color. All of the man's senses were attuned to his surroundings, just as ours are when we perceive color.

A person can "smell" colors through the nose, not, perhaps, through the olfactory system, but optically. What is seen can be smelled because people associate color with smell. Thus the perfume industry knows to produce cologne in colors of green, which represents nature and freshness. Pinks and lavenders produce sweet, light scents. Muskier perfumes are associated with ambers and deep yellows. The marketing industry also pushes certain "buy" buttons with color—everything from toasters to automobiles.

Humans also perceive colors through the sense of touch, which has a great deal to do with skin sensitivity to warm and cool colors. Synesthesia, the ability to hear colors and see sounds, is another element of a person's color sense.

In addition to the various senses of color, comes preferences, which tell people a great deal about themselves, much like analyzing handwriting in which certain strokes can be consciously altered to change unwanted personality traits. Use and preference of colors can be changed in order to bring about personal transformation or temporary behavior changes.

Alexander Schauss, clinical psychologist and director of the American Institute for Biosocial Research in Tacoma, Washington, is credited with developing a soft medium-pink paint used in prison holding cells throughout the United States. The color reportedly calms inmates, and possibly serves as an appetite suppresser.

Other research, though, indicates that the actual color of pink may not be the triggering mechanism that calms prisoners. Simply changing the color to any comforting shade can have the same effect. It is the change, from say a boring institutional green, to a pink, which is at the opposite side of the color spectrum, that calms inmates, according to Stanley Coren, psychology professor at the University of British Columbia in Vancouver. "If five years down the line you change it from pink to another color, it will have the same effect," Coren says.

Thus, even though some studies on color cause controversy, researchers know that something happens on a physiological and psychological level concerning color and light. These diversified opinions are offered in this book, and it is left to the reader to discern what is viable and usable in his or her own life.

Moods are changed by the reaction to sunny or rainy weather. When the sun is out, we are exposed to full-spectrum lighting. We see it as a form of white light, but it is actually a blending of all the colors in the spectrum. Too much gloomy, dark weather, and some people require medical intervention. Many are able to find rejuvenation during vacations because of contact with nature and its many natural colors.

While hiking in the mountains one spring day with a friend from the beach area of California, she remarked about the green lushness surrounding us on all sides. "I love my place at the beach, but this green does something for me. Maybe it's time for a change."

Without intellectualizing the nuances of color, she was moved by her green surroundings, which the ancients linked to growth, and rejuvenation.

At the onset of our visit, my friend, a world traveler, had talked about doing something constructive with her travels. She had just returned from the first experience involving her changed travel focus by serving two weeks as a construction worker with "Habitat for Humanity International," a volunteer organization that builds and refurbishes affordable homes for low-income families. Perhaps her newfound desire for green surroundings was mingling with her sense of growth and change.

An individual's current state of mind, and its reaction to specific colors, though, is not all that is at work when a person sees certain colors. Memories also help elicit various responses. In 1937 physician Felix Deutch was one of the first scientists to write about the emotional effects of color, which he thought was partly the result of memory association. Some people may feel peaceful in the face of green because they recall times spent in the mountains, close to nature. Red may bring to mind the warmth of a fireplace recalled from youth. An individual recalling an austere Sunday school teacher who always wore orange, may be turned off by that color. Or a person may remember a beloved grandfather who consistently wore blue shirts and, therefore, blue is considered a favorite color.

Or it can have the reverse effect. One woman says she likes the color blue, but it reminds her of her first husband who surrounded himself with blue—blue car, blue clothes, blue furniture—and therefore, she never uses blue herself.

Color also comes tumbling into the metaphysical world, sometimes in the guise of auras that surround the body, which some can see and discern. Auras, too, inhabit the mind and body in other ways, such as those seen in the beginning stages of an epileptic seizure or preceding a migraine headache.

Thus, color permeates every aspect of our lives. Humans are creatures of color—light and darkness, pale and bold, hot and cool, smooth and rough, in illness and in health, for good and bad, in mind, body, and spirit.

- Color has texture. It can be touched.
- Color is visual. It is seen through the eyes.
- Color can be heard if we listen with our hearts.
- Colors can be smelled, like the aroma of freshly cut grass.
- Color is psychological. It can be inwardly felt.
- Color is intuitive. People sense it.
- Color penetrates the body. It is physiological.
- Color is metaphysical, holistic, transcendental, and of the universe.

If color and light, then, are so pervasive in the lives of men and women, an understanding of its power, beauty, and magnetism can enrich a person's life. To ignore it is to deprive oneself of an opened treasure chest flowing endlessly with touchable rainbows. For it is not the pot of gold at the end of the rainbow that is worth seeking, but the splendor of the rainbow itself.

CHAPTER 1

How Colors Enter Our Lives

Many different theories of how people perceive color have existed through the ages. New findings made possible through modern technology and advanced scientific discoveries are shedding light on the intricacies of how the energy of light and the human mind and brain come together in concert to color the world.

An understanding of the way in which people are able to distinguish one color from another, and the cause behind this phenomenon, can only serve to enrich one's everyday brush with the world's multitude of colors.

COLOR IS PULSATING ENERGY

Sir Isaac Newton in the seventeenth century is credited with discovering the visible spectrum and diagrammed how light breaks into wavelengths of radiant energy. He invented the modern prism as people know it today, usually a transparent block of glass cut at various angles that reflects light waves of varying colors. Newton also discovered how light is bent, which laid a scientific foundation of the physics of light.

Johann Wolfgang von Goethe, an eighteenth century German poet, dramatist, and philosopher, refuted the wide acceptance of Newtonian color physics. He believed color was an interchange of light and shadow, or that it was more related to a degree of darkness created by shadows, such as that from candles, moonlight, sunlight, liquids, or crystals, among others. Yet, Newtonian physics prevailed.

Albert Einstein added to the knowledge of light and color by his theories on how the energy of light travels through the universe.

These early discoveries have been added to and altered as new theories and information concerning energy unfold to unlock the secrets of how people perceive or see certain wavelengths of this radiant energy, and how it affects the universe, the world, and ultimately individual lives.

The new science of chaos, though, is lending credibility to Goethe's theories. It isn't that Newton's theories are obsolete concerning color, but scientist and layperson alike know that more exists to color than a particular wavelength. Goethe's theory is holistic as opposed to Newton's, which is reductionist. Reductionism reduces a theory or statement to its least complex state. Goethe's theory on color expanded. He believed that color, including light waves, encompassed everything it experienced in its path as it journeyed toward planet earth.

When human perception of color is viewed holistically, as Goethe envisioned it, color then becomes a part of the entire pulsating universe, most of which is not observable to the naked eye, or even through the lens of sophisticated telescopes or other instruments. All sorts of matter floating about in the universe, such as planets, stars, dust particles and gas may be observable, but gravity and other known and suspected forms of matter and energy are not. Yet they all become a part of how humans see color.

Some theories hold that what people see as color may be an interruption—a coming together of certain energies that people see in an accumulated form, just as humans, or a chair, are forms of that same energy. If people see red instead of blue, it is because they're observing the lower frequency, or vibration of red, rather than the faster, or more frequent vibration of blue. But these initial vibrations of color may be influenced by other vibrations of which scientists only speculate. Through the electrons in the retinas of their eyes, people tune into these vibrations, internalize them, and color individual worlds. When understood this way, red is not the power color people have ascribed to it. Yet, it remains one of the easiest colors to perceive because the chromosomes in the human body are more adept at discerning red than blue, according to Myron Wolbarsht, biophysicist and professor of ophthalmology at Duke University. "We have few cells in the system that are attuned to blue," he says.

"Actually the brightest color for us is yellow, but red and green are the easiest for us to discern," says Wolbarsht. To test the difference in the ease of seeing yellow as opposed to blue, he suggests trying to read something in a blue light, and then read it under a yellow light. "You can almost not make out the form under blue light."

Perhaps the reaction to red has other psychological meanings, as in the "blood of life," or that what people project and feel, they see, which becomes a quantum, or even a chaos experience.

Fred Alan Wolf, a physicist and author of *Star Wave*, says that coming to terms with quantum physics means that scientists are responsible for their observations because they are a part of what is being observed. Again, it becomes a holistic experience. Like the scientists, people are not innocent bystanders in their daily observance of colors. Although people distinguish colors by activation of chiefly three light-absorbing chemicals, or pigments, in the eye (red, blue, and green), the observance is altered by conscious and unconscious perceptions, as well as what is going on in the world.

Since light is energy, and humans are forms of that same energy, humans step into the quantum world to make sense of color. Quantum theory holds that energy is not absorbed or radiated continuously but discontinuously, and is not infinitely divisible. In other words, it is not "fixed." Like man and woman, color is not "an island unto itself," but is affected by all life, or energy swirling about it. It can be likened to waves of colored energy that stop to pick up intergalactic hitchhikers on their trip to the eye's retina.

Scientists from a variety of disciplines, such as physicist Fritjof Capra, author of *The Tao of Physics*; Nobel Prize recipient Brian Josephson; and Beverly Rubrik, Ph.D., of Temple University, are discovering and making statements to the effect that the universe and all its dynamic parts are interrelated and of one holistic character, dependent upon one another. Josephson speculates that different parts of the universe may have contact with one another even from great distances, and Rubrik envisions a nonlocal field of consciousness that may interact with life.

These theories have everything to do with color, because people do not simply see colors with their eyes. All the senses are alive and alert to the sight, sound, smell, taste and extra sense of color. If people believe in the unity of the senses, a theory that was kicked around by the ancients, and which is gaining ground today among scientists, color becomes a dynamic of an outer and inner light, not simply seen with the eyes, but felt universally, and seen and felt individually.

EXPERIENCING COLOR

Anita Baroldi, a pilot from California, once related to me the high she gets from the surrounding colors when she's flying. She described the sensations of color as far more graphic in the air—like seeing the rainbow in vivid, solid colors. "You don't just catch a glimpse of violet. It's purple. The sky is a deeper blue than anything we see standing on the ground. And the tops of clouds are brilliantly silver, or sometimes gold. The outside of a storm cloud is multi-colored—deep rich colors. That's when you meet the rainbow," she says. When she's in the air all of her senses are more alive. She is able to grasp the miasma of color about her more energetically than when she is grounded. But also at work are the changed conditions from an earthbound existence. The air is thinner, more moisture is available, and fewer obstructions exist as light waves from the electromagnetic spectrum bounce from them and force the retinas of the eyes to take a peek.

"You can get in a thunderstorm at ten thousand feet and not know it's a thunderstorm until you hear someone in a jet at thirty-five thousand feet observing the thunderstorm you're in. Someone not so sensitive would say he was flying into a black cloud. But it's indigo black."

She also described one of the most dangerous clouds, an ice cloud, as green. "During the day or night if you see a greenish cloud you know it has ice in it, and you learn to avoid them."

She also described Elmo's Fire, an anomaly she's seen from the cockpit of older planes equipped with static wicks on the wings. "It looks like the window is on fire. It's caused by static electricity. You can put your finger on the Plexiglas and can make greenish, glowing patterns in an electrical storm."

What Baroldi describes is not a simple observation of color. Her feelings and interactions with the color bring it to life. It becomes a living, breathing, heart-felt experience. Such is the power and experience of color.

HOW PEOPLE SEE COLOR

Basically, color is reflected light from the sun. People both feel and see it, although what they feel and see are simply reflected rays of colored light emanating from the objects. The objects themselves have no color. But the sensation of color is aroused by the way people respond to the different wavelengths of light as they bounce off the object. An object, such as a leaf, appears green because it is reflecting the green waves in a portion of the electromagnetic spectrum, while absorbing the other colors. The type and amount of color an object absorbs is determined by its level of saturation or pigmentation.

Humans are able to see approximately 40 percent of the rays of light energy that make up certain wavelengths from a small part of the electromagnetic spectrum. Those that produce visible colors in this spectrum have become the "rainbow of color."

Many colors, though, exist in the electromagnetic spectrum, but the colors visible to humans run from wavelengths of red through orange, yellow, green, blue, indigo, and violet. Blue wavelengths, being the shortest, pack the most energy. The least energetic, although psychologically it has become the color of energy, is red. It is the longest visible color of the spectrum, so it is more diffused—stretched out further—than blue, the shortest wavelength.

People see only a certain portion of the electromagnetic spectrum because air molecules polarize light and filter only certain light vibrations to make them visible. The colors fade out entirely from human view as they reach the shorter rays of ultraviolet light on one side of the spectrum, and the longer rays of infrared light on the other side. Ultraviolet light contains smaller wavelengths than those able to be seen in the visible color spectrum. Overexposure to ultraviolet light can be dangerous, but a certain amount of it is necessary for the body to produce vitamin D. Sunglasses are now available that screen out most of the UV rays that cause damage to the eyes. Some also block out visible blue light, producing a sharper vision than regular glasses.

Infrared wavelengths are longer than those visible on the red end of the color spectrum. Special equipment is needed to view ultraviolet or infrared light.

Black, white, and gray represent the absence of light, although when all the colors of the spectrum of light are blended together, it becomes what we know as "white light," or is sometimes referred to as "additive light." Taken apart, or fragmented again, this white light becomes the colored spectrum.

If you can imagine grasping the rainbow in the palm of your hand and crunching all the colors together and then releasing it, white light would spill from your hands.

When these same colors are mixed in painting materials, though, the result is gray.

CREATING COLOR

The main or primary colors of the spectrum are blue, red, and green. When a person sees a multitude of colors in a rainbow, it is actually a blending of two or more of these three primary colors. People see different shades of blue in the sky because the nitrogen and oxygen molecules that scatter the light waves coming as blue are stronger and weaker in certain parts of the atmosphere. Looking straight up through the least atmosphere, people see only blue light. If a person looks toward the horizon, through stronger atmosphere, the longer wavelengths of other colors lessen the blue's intensity, and it becomes a lighter hue.

Like sound, colors reflect, refract, diffract, and interfere. Reflected light is like that coming back from a mirror. Paint pigments on canvas reflect color. The human body or a flower reflects specific colors. These colors as a person sees them are achieved when an object reflects a certain color from the spectrum while at the same time, absorbing and negating all other light or color.

A stained glass window appears extra rich in color because the glass is designed to block out all other wavelengths of the spectrum except those the artist wants the viewer to see. This response is called "transmitted" light.

The colors seen in a stained glass window differ from the way people see most colors because light passes through it instead of being reflected from it.

Refracted light is that which is scattered by elements such as water, or some solids. The extraordinary sunsets of oranges, deep pinks, and deep golds people have become accustomed to viewing in industrialized parts of the world are caused by scattered or refracted light—the result of light rays bumping into, and scattering from airborne, atmospheric pollutants.

Diffracted light is caused when a light ray is broken up into dark or light bands, or into separate colors of the spectrum through natural or unnatural interferences, such as passing light through a narrow slit. Colors that "interfere" are generated by disturbing or preventing certain wavelengths from manifesting themselves in their usual manner. In physics, when two wavelengths are interfered, they will either neutralize or reinforce one another. Likewise color that is neutralized or interfered with will either diminish or heighten in intensity.

Colors also become intense, have frequency, and mimic music's loudness, pitch, and tone through color, intensity, hue, and shade.

Hue is often called the "soul" of color. It accounts for an endless number of shades of the same color because they share a common "base" color. For instance: scarlet or vermilion red represent highly saturated red colors. The color rose is not so red because it is less saturated. Still, all three colors share the same base. Blue and violet, or green and chartreuse, share base colors. This degree of saturation in a hue is called "chroma." The lower the chroma, or saturation, the lower its brightness. Thus, soft or pale colors contain a low chroma.

Pure red or pure yellow are considered "warm" colors, and they generally make people feel warm and energetic since they are the colors of fire and the sun.

If placed on a traditional color wheel, the colors opposite the warm colors of red and yellow are the blue colors, which are considered cool and calming.

Colors also have mass, with brighter, darker ones appearing to be heavier or to have more volume. Fashion coordinators try to balance this volume by integrating a strong color with a weak one. They achieve this by minimizing the area covered by the strong one, and maximizing that of the weaker one.

AN EXPANDING RAINBOW OF COLORS

Until modern chemistry entered the picture humans lived comfortably with the colors of nature. With the advent of new dyes, the mind's eye became sensitive to an ever-expanding rainbow of colors. The eye can discern more than 2 million shades of color. Yet, only seven thousand of them have been named and classified. Black, white, and gray are not technically considered colors at all, but in studying the effects of color on humans, most scientists include them as colors.

The colors in the countryside could be considered "natural." Those in the city, "unnatural" or artificial, although they have become as natural to city dwellers as the green of an open field. They all affect the senses and the sensibilities because they are given substance through electromagnetic energy, whether that be from the electrons in the human retina, or the sun and, ultimately, from the swirling universe.

HOW COLOR AFFECTS THE BRAIN

The light or color spectrum is caused by vibrations of electromagnetic energy that travel from the sun. They penetrate the body through the eyes and skin and send signals to the brain. At the same time, everything else in the world comes into play. For example: If a person is looking at a red rose growing in the garden, his or her sense of sight is affected by the surrounding noise, temperature, and even the person's own mood.

All of these sensations create neuronal activity in various parts of the brain, but commingle to form a personal perception of the red rose. The same red rose may appear vibrant to one person and, perhaps, dull to another.

Too, colors stimulate an emotional and mental response, such as strong and weak energy. But the human body responds to some degree to each vibrating color. A person can intellectually accept or reject the sensations, but is affected by the colors nonetheless.

Studies at Washington University School of Medicine in St. Louis show that certain parts of the visual cortex, an area in the back of the brain that discerns what the eye sees, are enhanced when a person focuses on a particular aspect of an object, such as its color. This can occur before the person sees the object or color. The brain is already primed for it to happen.

For example, in primitive hunting cultures, the brain was already preparing itself for the movement of animals in the forest before the movement occurred. Today, a person may be given directions to an attorney's office and told to look for a blue sign on the building. His or her brain is already preparing for the blue sign, and the person has an immediate response, sometimes of comfort, when he or she spots the sign because the brain is satisfied.

Maurizio Corbetta, M.D., research instructor at Washington University School of Medicine, says that the specialized areas of the visual cortex sift through and process the selected information, such as color. Researchers have been able to observe blood flow changes in subjects' brains during this sorting process. "If a stimulus such as color is being attended to, the frequency of neuronal firing increases in a specific region of the brain," says Corbetta.

"When a person thinks about a particular characteristic such as color, the information is directed to a certain visual association area. So the brain may actually be stimulated in that particular area before the color is spotted," says Corbetta. In other words, a person could be anticipating a certain color, as in the case of looking for someone he or she knows who has red hair (or the blue sign mentioned earlier), and the brain would be at work in a specific area geared to discern the color before ever spotting the person with the red hair. Or in less time that portion of the brain may be activated when a

person spots a friend in a crowded room by first recognizing
him or her wearing a favorite orange sweater.

"You can make visual connections with color. I think when
the visual field is cluttered, and you can't get any clear, particular
feature, color becomes more important. Such as when you find
red, something in the brain goes boom," says Corbetta.

"This type of association may be evolutionary. When
man hunted in the forests, motion was more important than
color. So the brain was ready to be stimulated by movement.
It was primed, and waiting. Maybe the brain is more receptive
now to color stimulation, because it is so cluttered with the
movement about us all the time," says Corbetta. Color
association cuts though the maze of movement.

Another theory that hasn't yet been proven, but that is
believed by some, such as Carlton Wagner who heads the
Institute for Color Research in Santa Barbara, is that people
have an automatic, and inherited endocrine gland response to
color. Carlton and others say that about 20 percent of an
individual's optic fibers go directly to the pituitary gland, a part
of the body's endocrine system, which also involves other
types of glands. The glands are part of the autonomic nervous
system that elicits involuntary action from certain parts of the
body, such as blushing when a person is embarrassed. Trying
to halt the blush is nearly impossible.

Stanley Coren, psychology professor at the University of
British Columbia and author of Sensation and Perception, the
most widely used textbook on visual perception in North
America, disagrees with Wagner's theory. He says color
perception is far more psychological than physiological.
Conditioning is a key factor in response to color. "The reason
we tend to think of yellows and reds as warm, and the blues
and violets as cool is a learned response," says Coren. "We
see blues and purples at twilight when there's not much heat

around, and we see reds and yellows at dawn when the earth is warming, so we refer to them as warm colors."

THE BRAIN'S PAL: THE RETINA

All people have small natural blind areas on each retina, but the brain fills in the missing portion in a manner that can be likened to hearing a pianist who misses a few notes. Listeners tend to fill in the missing notes. When color is at play, the brain automatically fills in the blind spots.

The retina is the largest user of the brain's neurons, taking up about 30 percent of the cortex, compared to hearing which encompasses about 3 percent. The brain's neurons are fed by 150 million light-sensitive cone and rod cells that act within two optic nerves, each consisting of about a million fibers. From these optic nerves, light sensations are relayed to a portion of the thalamus that also serves other sensory input, and from there to the primary visual cortex. Then they travel to numerous other specialized areas of the brain.

Corbetta says the primary visual cortex is also known as V1, and that after entering that area the signals are relayed into another processing area called V2, and from there they branch out and interact with other sensory areas that detect not only color, but actions such as movement, shape, brightness, and depth. If a sensory area is manipulated, say by changing the brightness or shading of a color, it can distort the entire perception.

An example of this distortion is observable when viewing a film's negative. What normally is dark or light can be reversed, but an individual in such a picture often can't be identified because the changed shading distorts perception.

INDIVIDUAL COLOR PERCEPTION

Some believe that as people become more in touch with their feelings, they see more colors or are sensitive to other colors produced, or blended, in the spectrum. Although this particular theory hasn't been proven, research by Jeremy Nathans, M.D., and Shannath L. Merbs, molecular biologist at Johns Hopkins University, shows that genetic variations in a gene that controls color vision make it possible for some people to see subtle differences in colors that are imperceptible to others.

The thousands of colors people see are caused by the initial activation and wavelength stimulation of the red, green, and blue light-absorbing chemicals, or pigments, in the eye. The brain then precisely calculates how much each pigment was activated and determines the exact color people see.

But what a person sees varies by the type of pigment with which he or she is genetically endowed. For example, two types of red-sensitive pigment have been identified and studied in a test tube.

The gene for each of the two red-sensitive pigments is found on the X chromosome. That means that men, who have only one X chromosome, can have only one or the other pigment, while some women will have genes for both types of pigment. Genetically, men have X-Y chromosomes, and women have X-X chromosomes, which would give women a greater chance for the doubled red-sensitive pigment. About 60 million women in the United States have this doubled exposure, according to Nathans.

Thus it's possible that women with both kinds of red-sensitive pigments can see more subtle variations in many base colors.

COLOR BLINDNESS

Color blindness is generally a deficiency in the perception of red and green. It is caused by activating certain pigments in the retina that are determined at this genetic level.

During World War II, men who were color blind were first exempted from service. Later it was discovered that an inability to discern green had positive connotations. They could more clearly spot camouflaged men and equipment in jungles because they weren't encumbered by the green surroundings.

Color blindness, though, is not generally perceived as an advantage. Studies at Johns Hopkins Medical Institutions show that among Caucasians, 8 percent of males and 1 percent of females differ in their color vision from the rest of the population. According to researchers there, color-blind people have hybrid genes in the retina. Normally, as discussed earlier, color is determined when different wavelengths of light stimulate the eye's red, green, and blue sensitive pigments. Specialized cone-shaped cells in the eye that contain light-absorbing pigments that are sensitive to specific bands of color pass this information on to the brain. The brain calculates this activity and determines what color is seen.

When a person carries the hybrid genes, though, he or she isn't as sensitive to red or green light. That person doesn't see red and green the same as the majority of the population because the brain ultimately shows them a different shade or color.

A new theory has been proposed by wife and husband research team, Maureen and Jay Neitz, the former an assistant professor of ophthalmology and cellular biology at the Medical College of Wisconsin, and the latter an assistant professor of cellular biology and anatomy at the same college. Their studies show that color blindness of all types may be the result of randomly dropped genes rather than the absence of one of the three main genes that code for red, blue, and green. Former theories held that color blindness occurred when one type of cone pigment was lost, or was replaced by an abnormal one. However, discoveries in the 1980s showed that many people have more than three color genes, and that the genes responsible for color vision have diverse coding patterns.

Recent studies also show that people with normal vision do not all see colors the same, which can be accounted for by this diverse coding pattern.

Perhaps, then, it's senseless when two people argue about whether a certain color is blue, or blue/green. It is a matter of perception determined by the diversity in the coding patterns of particular individuals. In other words, color, like beauty, can be in the eye of the beholder.

COLOR AND SMELL

Some people associate certain smells with color. Scientists know that certain smells evoke memories, or can change a person's moods. The pathways to smell are located in the limbic system, an array of related nervous system structures located in the midbrain. These structures are associated with feelings, such as anger, fear, sexual arousal, pleasure, and sadness. So a person can smell a certain odor and be reminded of his or her childhood. Humans can discern about five thousand different odors, but like color, the odors can smell different to those experiencing them. Robert Henkin, M.D., of the Taste and Smell Clinic in Washington, D.C., says the initial difference in experience is genetic. People inherit a certain amount of odor sense. Some inherit very little odor sense at all.

Just as some people are color blind, certain individuals are "odor blind," according to Chuck Wysocki, researcher at the Monell Chemical Senses Center in Philadelphia. "And it can be inherited," he says.

Even people with little sense of smell, though, can learn to associate certain odors with particular colors.

Some of the standard colors associated with smell include:

- **Black and other dark shades**—dusky sophistication
- **Cinnamon**—spice and the orient
- **Violet**—femininity and flowers
- **Blue**—clear and refreshing
- **Ivory**—subdued sophistication
- **Gray**—conservative and correct
- **Yellow**—cleanliness
- **Lavender**—subdued energy

One such color/smell response is the use of lavender in office buildings to increase work efficiency and lessen mental fatigue, or to awaken hotel guests with a refreshing lemon scent, according to commercial fragrance researchers.

COLOR AND SOUND

School children, when asked to match colors to sounds, associate violet and blue with low-sound frequencies. The sound of a trumpet has been linked to bright red according to Richard Restak, M.D., author of *The Brain*.

In the eighteenth century, the world's first color organ was invented. It had a keyboard that produced certain colors of light with each depressed note.

The musical work "Prometheus" by nineteenth century composer Aleksandr Scriabin included a part for a color organ.

Synesthesia, or color hearing, whereby one hears colors and sees sounds, is widely accepted today. Peter Himmelman's album cover by the same name, describes synesthesia as a state of sensory reversal wherein one hears colors and sees sounds.

But the theory of color hearing was first treated scientifically by English philosopher John Locke in an essay published in 1690, followed by ophthalmologist Theodore Woodhouse's (also an Englishman) comparative table of sounds and colors.

Cecil Stokes, in the first half of the twentieth century, created Auroratone films that set music to color. His was the forerunner to light festivals, discotheque, electric light parades, and the use of mind spas, popular today with the advent of electronic technology. His techniques were also used on psychotic patients. French composer Olivier Messiaen claimed he could see the color of a tone.

Wassily Kandinsky, author of *The Rainbow Book*, compared musical sounds to colors. The light, warm reds and medium yellows were seen as strong like the sounds of trumpets. Cool reds, were more like violins. Kandinsky's drum was orange-red, and he saw church bells as pure orange. Yellow he perceived as a bugle, and the flute music was blue. Darker blue was the cello and darkest blue or black were made by the organ. Woodwinds he heard as violet.

Lawrence Lee, author of *An Appreciation of Stained Glass*, likens the art of stained glass to music by saying that light waves shift along a portion of the spectrum according to the color of the glass they penetrate, activating the retina with a direct effect similar to the sound waves that activate the ear drum.

COLOR AND TOUCH

Two particular cases involving the sense of touch and color were recorded by *Life* magazine in the 1960s. One was a Russian girl who could distinguish red, green, and blue with her fingers. Another woman, from Michigan, described certain colors as rough, sticky, or smooth. She considered light blue the smoothest, yellow as slippery, and the darker colors of red, green, and dark blue as sticky. She described violet as "rough."

However, later research showed that what the blind women were really sensing was heat. Brighter colors at the long end of the visible electromagnetic spectrum reflects more light, and people with sensitive skin can pick up these subtle distinctions.

Stanley Coren, authority on the senses, says the sensitivity of some individuals who are blind enables them to "read" reasonable size print of eighteen points or above by discerning the warm areas or shapes. When their hands were cooled, they were unable to "read" with their hands.

I asked a friend, Mike Zorick of Indio, California, who has been blind since birth, about seeing colors through other senses. Zorick has competed in a number of national tournaments for blind athletes. "I met many blind athletes at these tournaments and none of them ever mentioned being able to tell colors by their touch or smell. I have never been able to tell colors by touch or smell. I have no idea what any color looks like. As far as I'm concerned, colors have names but no meaning.

"I do have a close friend who went blind when he was a teenager. He has been blind for almost forty years. He still remembers how the various colors looked and he remembers how other things appeared. He even has visual things in his dreams. When I dream, there is nothing visual. My friend is also a long-distance runner. When he runs a race, he asks his partner to describe the surroundings. This helps him to refresh his visual memory."

OTHER COLOR-VISION CRITTERS

Although humans are not as adept at smell and taste as other animals, their visual systems are more highly developed. Yet, most mammals have visual systems similar to humans, according to Wolbarsht. Some, though, are able to discern colors in the ultraviolet range. Any differences in visual systems develop for survival purposes, he says. "It's all a matter of evolution. Fish who live in caves have degenerative eyes. Rats who live at poor light levels lose some color vision because they don't have to use it. Cats have color vision but they don't use it. They are more interested in intensity—brightness—because it's more useful to them."

Some even have no sight at all. A colony of blind spiders, similar to the common trap-door spider, was discovered in caves in the Australian Outback in 1991. It's believed they have inhabited the desert for more than 3 million years.

We have assumptions about how other critters see color, sometimes based on folklore. We tend to think of bulls being turned on to red, but Wolbarsht says goldfish, too, are turned on by red.

Brian Harris, entomology curatorial assistant at the Natural History Museum of Los Angeles County, says that since most insects see in the ultraviolet range they actually don't see the same colors as humans. Thus, when we say that a particular insect is turned on by blue, it means the color as humans see it, when, in fact, the insect may be seeing yellow.

"If you want to attract a Morpho butterfly cover yourself with a blue cloth because the color attracts them. That's because they have solid blue on their wings (through human perceptions), and it's a sexual attraction. That's how they are attracted to mates," says Harris.

Harris says most of the colors that attract insects are sexual responses. Few spiders, though, see colors. Their eyes are geared to darkness. Movement and shape are more important to them, says Blaine Herbert, a member of the Arachniphobia Society, and professor of biology at Pasadena City College in California. "Some color vision has been detected in jumping spiders, though, because they are daytime creatures. They probably have some infrared detectors."

Other critters have color preferences:

- Mosquitoes are drawn to the darker colors of blue, red, and brown.
- Flies aren't drawn to the color blue. Thus barn stalls are often painted blue.
- Bees are attracted to bright colors.
- Birds are attracted to reds, but are nearly blind to blue.
- Deep-water fish respond to deep blues.
- Swallowtail butterflies are attracted to red.
- Certain fireflies depend on flashing colors for attraction.
- Tropical click beetles use flashing colors for attraction.

So humans share colors with other sighted creatures, although what humans perceive as a particular color may be a very different color to them. Likewise, what one individual perceives as a certain color, may appear slightly different to another. Therefore, color, as a person sees it, is not simply a solid entity, but part of the entire cosmology of a pulsating universe.

CHAPTER 2

The Color of Auras

Auric phenomenon has been recorded since about 500 B.C. How much further into the twilight of man it existed, one can only guess. Throughout the centuries, though, scholars, scientists, physicians, and spiritualists have written in different forms about the energy or light fields, composed of waves or particles, or both, that surround humans, or all "things." This energy that surrounds humans is sometimes referred to as the human energy field.

John White, in *Future Science*, says that ninety-seven different cultures make references to auric phenomenon using many different names.

Auras, though, are not limited to events happening outside the body. Under certain conditions, such as at the beginning of epileptic seizures or migraine headaches, people experience auras. Certain types of visualization can also produce auras, such as the chakra body system of energy.

Color, then, has its place in both the scientific and metaphysical worlds. And the two continually rub and bump into one another, sometimes blending into an experience that crosses the boundaries and sends rays of enlightenment and understanding into both camps.

VIBRATIONS OF COLORED AURAS

All matter in the universe is associated with, and emits, vibration, movement, and frequency. These vibrations affect all human senses—touch, hearing, smell, taste, and sight. Thus, the energy of color, which encompasses a particular vibrational, electromagnetic wavelength, is linked to all other energy in the cosmos. Harmonious, vibrational linking between persons or things is called "tonal resonance." This interconnectedness, applied to individuals who are sensitive to these connecting relationships, is sometimes referred to as "vibrational empathy."

Physicist David Bohm has suggested that particles and people both influence one another because everything in the universe is connected to everything else in the universe, including the past, present, and future. He calls it "implicate order." Particles are not separated, but connected in such a way that it makes them invisible to ordinary concepts of reality. He suggests that with humans, such a theory might explain extrasensory perception (ESP)—the ability for people to be in tune with one another to the extent that they develop common notions at the same time.

Many people believe the vibrational energy of color surrounding plants and animals emits auras that some people are able to see. People who see auras might be endowed with a form of vibrational empathy, or Bohm's common notion theory, referred to as the implicate order theory.

Whatever the source or cause of the aura, people from all walks of life are tapping into the experience as never before.

- A biologist being interviewed relates that his girlfriend routinely reads his aura, and that his parents read each other's auras.
- During a seminar on creativity, actress Ellen Burstyn recounted that during filming of *Resurrection*, in which she starred and was nominated for an Academy Award for her performance as a psychic healer, the woman whose story was being told and who served as a consultant on the set, gave her a daily "aura fluff" to boost her energy.
- A woman practicing yoga to alleviate the effects of multiple sclerosis tells of how she uses the auras of the chakra system for balance and energy.

All auric experience, though, is associated with other forms of energy occurring within the brain, the entire body, or within energy fields swirling about the world and the universe. It may be a form of energy we are only beginning to understand.

RECAPTURING THE AURA

The ancients believed the body emitted auric light, and throughout history halos, jewels, and certain ornaments have been used by people to stand for the spiritual energies that radiate from the body.

Edgar Cayce was among the many mystics who claimed to see auras surrounding people. He once wrote in *Auras* that he associated people with colors in reds, blues, and greens surrounding their heads and shoulders. He was not familiar with the term "aura," and assumed others saw these same colors.

In the traditional auric world red stood for energy and force; orange for thoughtfulness; yellow for health and well-being; green for healing; blue for the color of the spirit; and indigo and violet were related to spiritual experiences. Cayce, like many spiritualists, believed white was the color of the soul in perfect balance.

Barbara B. Brown, in her book, New Mind, New Body, says the skin sees in Technicolor, and that these colors are picked up by the brain through the eye and expressed electrically by the skin, forming auras.

The body's electronic or magnetic fields are measured through modern technology with devices such as the electrocardiogram, which records the electric current which the heart muscle produces, or the electroencephalogram, which records the electric impulses made by a person's brain cells.

Changes in brain-wave activity are recorded according to the frequencies they produce. Thus, various states of mind record different frequencies. For example:

- The beta state, which is the normal, wide-awake, working state, produces one of the higher frequencies.
- The alpha state, such as daydreaming while driving the car on a long stretch of road when there is no stress, records a lower frequency.
- The theta state, which generally occurs just before falling asleep or awakening, and which is considered the mind's most creative period, produces less frequency.
- The delta state of sleep which is the harbinger of dreams and nightmares, records even less frequency. But even sound asleep, the brain is always at work.

More than fifty of these different states exist, interspersed between the four just mentioned. So it is possible that certain states can produce, or respond to, auras which also have specific frequencies related to the vibrations of different colors.

AN EXPERIENCE WITH AURAS

Madeleine Conklin, an artist and bookkeeper, who lives in Big Bear City, California, had her first experiences seeing auras as a child. At that time, she assumed everyone saw them.

"I would wake up and see the colors. They are very structured colors. I would see an outline on the frame of a mirror. Just outside that frame, there would be another frame of light. It wasn't misty. It had a real definite straight, or curved line to the edges. And then, sometimes, I would just see the floating bubbles of light. They would be like lint particles. But they would be all in colors. I didn't think anything was unusual until I started pointing to them and saying, 'Did you see that?' And that's when I found out others weren't seeing them.

"When I was older, maybe I would be reading and would see round pillars of light in whitish or golden colors. I wasn't brave enough, but I wanted to get up and go step into these pillars. I knew they weren't solid. I wanted to go stand in them and see if they did anything to my body. But I didn't. I would just look at them.

"At times, when someone had died in my family, it would be like a swirling ball of light that would come into my room. And I would ask them questions. It would be like my uncle who passed away. It's almost like something was breathing. It would keep its form but it would expand and contract."

Later, in married life, she experienced a similar sensation when she saw an aura associated with her husband. He was listening to music she described as very relaxing. The music, though, had made him feel very emotional. "He described it as 'the leaving of a great love.'"

"What was different about that one, though, was that there were three distinct colors. When my uncle came, it was like two colors sort of blended. The colors near my husband went straight up and seemed to go past the ceiling. In the center, was a form, but big in comparison to my husband. It was blue in the center. It had a bright pink, small edge around it, and then white on the outer edge that was wider than the pink edge. This form, also, seemed to breath. It would go out and come back. It kept its form, though. It stayed there the whole time he had the emotion. I asked him to turn around and look at it, but he couldn't see it. And then it appeared to just fade. But while it was there, I couldn't see the wall behind it."

When the episode ended, she typed in the experience on her computer. "I still get shivers when I read it."

"The colors are fun, and make me feel good since I'm an artist. It's like finding a toy. Something new to play with."

Madeleine's aura episodes are all spontaneous. She never concentrates and tries to make one appear. Sometimes in church she sees them around the speaker. "When he is really excited and energetic you can see the aura going out of him, and when he becomes more calm, it goes down a little. Sometimes I will see different colors on a person. When someone is sharing something that is hurtful and painful, the colors seem to be darker—purples and reds. If it's something that was exhilarating, it will be in golds, and pinks and light blues. Sometimes, it will appear to be as though this shadowy figure or outline—a human shadow—is standing outside him, and beside him. My impression at that time is that the person is being guided or helped by this energy to relay whatever he or she needs to at the time. It's like this energy is giving the person support."

Madeleine says she doesn't know what causes her to see the auras—whether it is all happening in her own brain, or whether it really is "out there."

"But I feel what I am actually seeing is generated by individuals. They usually enjoy hearing about it. When I feel the energy is not theirs, but rather a guide, I ask my higher self if I should tell them what I saw. So sometimes I don't."

She also sometimes sees mass auras in the early evenings around trees and flowers, as if they are all radiating auras in unison.

"Usually the colors are more in the pastels in the evening."

Madeleine has never seen her own aura around her head, which is what many auric readers aim for. "But I have seen them around my hands when I'm doing my art work."

With her eyes closed she also sees three-dimensional scenes. If she is visualizing a tree and a lake, everything becomes more vivid than in real life. She describes the motion of the trees and water as "very fluid." The scenes usually never last more than ten seconds, "but it is an overwhelming feeling, and I get caught up in the breathing of the trees."

"I finally came to a conclusion that they are a part of my life. I used to think it was just something interesting, but now I have more of a curiosity about it. Color is very important in my life," she says.

AURAS AND HEALING

It is believed that in "laying on of hands" an energy flow is taking place between the practitioner and the patient. The healer, who has a wide corona or aura, is transferring energy to the patient, whose corona is narrow or weak.

In the 1980s, physiologist Dr. Valorie Hunt, then at the University of California, Los Angeles, recorded the frequency of low millivoltage signals from the body during a series of rolfing sessions. At the same time The Rev. Rosalyn Bruyere of the Healing Light Center in Glendale, California, observed the auras of both the rolfer and the person being rolfed. Her comments on the color, size, and energy movements of the chakras and auras involved were recorded by Hunt.

Hunt and her staff then mathematically analyzed the wave patterns being recorded during the rolfing sessions. The wave pattern forms and frequencies which mimicked specific colors in the color spectrum were the same as those observed and recorded by The Rev. Bruyere, a Pasadena, California, health practitioner. If the frequency analysis recorded a green energy field in a particular area of the body being rolfed, so did Bruyere. The same experiments were repeated with other aura readers and shown to be the same as Bruyere's.

Hunt, who continues her studies in private practice today, says the chakra areas that were rolfed often displayed the same colors stated in the metaphysical literature, such as Kundalini-red, hypogastric-orange, spleen-yellow, heart-green, throat-blue, third eye-violet, and crown-white.

Hunt is now working with the mathematics of Chaos patterning since color as we see it has a limited spectrum of visibility. James Gleick, writing in *Chaos: Making a New Science*, says that pioneering Chaos scientists in the 1970s were examining "the invisible forms that order takes in nature." Hunt says, though, that the earlier studies, though dated, and not incorporating Chaos, have held up. She now trains healers throughout the country and works on development of new equipment to be used to evaluate touch healing practices and how they affect the healer and the disease. Her work is chronicled in a forthcoming book, *Infinite Mind: The Science of Human Vibrations*.

"If the healer comes in and heals it, he or she has ideas about how it works, such as tapping into specific spectrum patterns, but they don't intellectually know how it works," says Hunt. Using Chaos patterning, she hopes to add the intellectual, scientific approach. "We're looking for the frequency pattern of the disease before it ever enters the body."

Hunt believes the patterns for disease are evident in the energy fields surrounding and inside the body prior to an attack on the body. "We want to pick it up before it becomes what we call disease."

"As long as we are locked into a medical model that only cures symptoms, we are behind the times. I work in the energy field of the entire person. We look for disturbances in that field that might eventually find its way into a pathological condition. There is a lot of good work that is being done with light and sound radiation, but it is still partly guesswork.

"We have come to the point where we don't argue with some people in the scientific community. They are behind the times. There was a time we could argue about the atom, too, but that is past. The National Institutes of Health (NIH) in Bethesda, Maryland, has created money for this type of research, and they've asked me to apply for a grant," says Hunt.

Hunt is referring to the new division of the NIH's multifaceted institutes that regularly supports about two thousand basic research projects, a few of which are housed in off-campus facilities throughout the United States and abroad. In 1992, $2 million was appropriated to establish an Office of Alternative Medicine (OAM) at the National Institutes of Health as the result of actions by former Congressman Berkeley Bedell, a Democrat from Iowa who served from 1975 to 1986. The office supports research, but does not endorse alternative medical practices. Bedell believes he was cured of a recurrence of prostate cancer by unconventional methods.

The American Medical Association says that since most alternative medical treatments remain unproven, they need scientific evaluation of the sort offered through the OAM. Thus far, though, proponents of alternative remedies have been unable to produce the type of scientific research and data required of traditional medical practices to support their claims.

THE CHAKRAS TAKE ON AURAS

According to Eastern tradition the body contains seven life force centers called chakras running parallel to the spine, and from there to the top of the head. They are part of a person's auric energy within the body, and control the inflow and outflow of the life force, *chi*, or life's energy. The chakras are also associated with certain colors.

- The first chakra, or root, is associated with the sex glands (or gonads), and is located at the base of the spine. It is also the base of the healing force of Kundalini, which connects and reinforces all the other chakras. This first chakra is seen as red.
- The second chakra is found at the mid-point in the abdomen, and is associated with the spleen, liver, and pancreas. This chakra's color is orange.
- The third chakra is slightly higher than the abdomen in the solar plexus area, and is associated with the adrenal glands. It is believed that anxiety and fear are associated with this area, and thus greatly affects a person's health. A first symptom may be stomach problems. Its color is yellow.
- The fourth chakra, which serves as a filtering system for the life force, and is situated in the

center of the chest area. It is associated with the center of the heart, and takes one into the beginning stages of the higher creative levels. It represents unconditional love. Color it green.

- The fifth chakra is found in the throat area, and stands for the thyroid gland. The second of the higher creative levels, some claim it represents the ability to channel to nonphysical entities. It can be an area of tension, accounting for headaches and throat problems. This chakra is considered blue.

- The sixth chakra is located in the middle of the forehead and relates to the pituitary gland. In metaphysics, it is associated with the third eye, and represents spiritual possibilities. Its color is indigo.

- The seventh chakra emanates from the area of the pineal gland, and is sometimes imaged as the center of a crown. It is symbolic of the "higher-self," which C. J. Jung, the father of archetypal psychology, characterized as the divine center of the psyche that sends images to the ego. It is necessary for growth and development to tap into the higher self in order to overcome the everyday lower-self. The higher-self is responsible for creativity, insight, enlightenment. It is white, and sometimes violet.

A person can visualize the chakras in a clockwise, spinning motion. Examine the spin of each chakra by beginning with the first level at the base of the spine and working upward, envisioning each level in the mind's eye.

Study and reflect on each chakra until it is a clear and bright color. When the seventh chakra is reached, visualize a release of all negative energy through the top of the head, and feel the energizing release throughout the body.

The colors can swirl about the body in a variety of patterns and colors for different people unless a person visualizes specific colors when dealing with the chakras.

GENERAL MEANINGS OF AURIC COLORS

Separate from the chakra system, but in some cases similar, are general meanings associated with auric colors. They are:

- **Black**—hate, evil, bias, judgment
- **Blue (dark)**—integrity, religion
- **Blue (light)**—devotion, healing, high ideals, spiritual attainment
- **Blue (indigo)**—vision, intuition, telepathy
- **Blue (royal)**—honesty, loyalty, dependability
- **Brown (dull)**—selfishness
- **Brown (orangish)**—repression, lack of ambition
- **Gray**—depression, sorrow, grief
- **Gray (green tint)**—deceit, bitterness, disease
- **Green (bright)**—sympathy
- **Green (emerald)**—healing ability, empathy
- **Orange**—pride, energy, ambition, curiosity, humanistic
- **Pink shades**—devotion, friendships, love of family, a childlike nature
- **Red (bright)**—sexuality, courage, egotism
- **Red (deep)**—anger, energy, change
- **Red (purple)**—power, of the world
- **Red (warm)**—affection
- **Red (orangish)**—healing, renewing
- **Violet**—spirituality, artistic, transforming

- **White**—pure, uplifting, integrated
- **Yellow (pale)**—illness
- **Yellow (vivid)**—intellect, curiosity, adventure
- **Yellow (golden)**—creativity, striving, spiritual quest

Clear bright colors indicate a confident and healthy state. Dull colors show negative energy. An auric field showing holes or vacant spaces indicates potential illness or imbalances in the mental, physical, and spiritual realm of an individual.

READING YOUR OWN AURA

Many people simply see auras spontaneously. For others, it takes practice.

To begin, sit in front of a mirror in a dimly lighted room. Relax and concentrate on the aura to be seen around your head in the mirror for several minutes (the time decreases with practice). Many people who see auras, though, rely on the spontaneity of observation. They simply appear when least expected.

KIRLIAN PHOTOGRAPHY

Kirlian, or radiation-field, photography has captured auras in photos, according to some adherents. Promoted in the late 1930s in the former Soviet Union by husband and wife Valentina and Semyon Kirlian, its beginnings go back further still to the 1890s when electrographic photos were displayed at a Russian exhibition. Its study became popular in the United States in the 1970s.

Pioneer in the U.S. studies, Kendal Johnson, built the first Kirlian photo equipment and worked with Thelma Moss,

Ph.D., then of the University of California, Los Angeles, whose name became forever linked to research on the subject. Moss is considered a pioneer in the United States on the scientific study of various forms of parapsychology.

Kirlian photography produces a photographic plate believed to be the aura or energy that emanates from animals and plants and that indicates physiological and emotional states of the mind and body.

The procedure is quite simple. The early photographs were made by placing the object in direct contact with film on a metal plate, and then administering a small jolt of electricity. Later studies produced photographs without the use of electricity.

The procedure could even be accomplished by picking up the electricity generated when one scrapes his or her feet across the carpet and then makes contact with someone else. In this case, though, when the slight amount of electricity is released, the person can touch his or her finger to the film, according to Moss, author of *The Body Electric*.

Kirlian-type photographs have captured the before and after hands of spiritual healers, showing fingertip coronas. Some studies have shown that after a healing, the healer's "aura" or corona is reduced, and the corona of the person receiving the healing has grown.

Some studies have claimed to detect disease states detected by Kirlian process before they have been diagnosed using traditional methods. Researchers in the United States found that a wider, and more brilliant corona existed when subjects were in a state of relaxation or during yogic breathing exercises, and that a red blotch appeared when the subjects were tense or angry.

Many of the studies employed the use of psychic healers whose fingers were electrophotographed at rest and during healing processes. The photos of fingers during healing had portions of bright auras and those at rest had none.

Although Hunt believes that an energy field exists, she says the validity of the earlier Kirlian photography was difficult to access scientifically because no natural frequencies existed. It was based on introducing 75,000 volts into the body to make it radiate, and capturing that radiation on film.

Detractors say that the three components of moisture, heat, and weight account for the "Kirlian field."

Yet, Hunt is quick to praise the efforts of researchers such as Moss. Scientists such as Thelma Moss are often derided by their peers. It is interesting to note, though, that Moss was one of the first in the United States to try to understand the basis for acupuncture, and its attendant chi. Her research involved photographing this flow of energy. She received skeptical review by her peers less than fifteen years ago. Today, acupuncture is gaining the recognition it deserves in the traditional medical community.

Too, Moss retained a healthy skepticism toward unorthodox practitioners making claims of miraculous cures, and sent many away from her doorstep. She found some of the other claims of Kirlian photography, such as those claiming to show how spirits enter a body, or life readings, as disreputable and damaging to more scientific studies.

FIRLD PHOTOGRAPHY

Stephen Cox, of Mystic Journey Services in Santa Monica, California, is a Firld photographer and interpreter. He describes Firld photography as linked to Kirlian photography.

Firld photography employs energy frequencies that are picked up from the hand which is held on an electromagnetic plate linked to color frequencies on a computer. At the same time the hand is placed on the plate, a photograph is taken of the head area that reflects what the computer establishes from the energy of the hand. That energy is correlated to the frequencies of the electromagnetic spectrum, and superimposed, via the computer, onto a picture of the head area.

Cox says the stability of the color is more important than the color itself. That is, breaks, holes, or gaps in the aura indicate interruptions to the normal, healthy flow of the aura. Although medical diagnosis is not the domain of Firld photographers, he says, "If a big gap exists in the aura, it means something is draining the life force."

In Firld photography the left side (which refers to colors on the individual's left side and not the left side of the picture) is considered the vibration entering the body. The right side expresses the energy, or vibrational frequency others feel or perceive around you. It is what you are putting out into the world.

The color rising above the head is an individual's inward experience, and the one that best represents the person's own motivations. The colors that predominate stand for certain characteristics. "With an angry person, it usually shows a lot of red," says Cox.

Cox says most people have an aura photo taken for the fun of it, but he believes it could be used in a physician's office to indicate that something might be wrong with the person if the aura is broken, or if it has a large gap. "I see it as validation of what people already know," says Cox, who explained that many people who get an aura photo already sense that something is wrong, and they are looking for something that will tell them to take action on it.

Aura photography, using the Firld process, ascribes some of the following meanings to colors, as seen in the aura.

- **White** is seen surrounding highly motivated individuals. It has the qualities of all the colors, but tends to be unstable. It denotes a healing ability or experience for the individual or those around him or her.
- **Violet** is mystical and magical, portending spiritual evolution. Violet indicates a high degree of sensitive intimacy, and the qualities of enchantment, charm, eroticism, and deep spiritual understanding.
- **Blue** shows feelings for peace, love, loyalty, truth, trust, contentment, and affection. Blue is the color of the communicator, especially in the ability to listen to others. It can mean peace along the spiritual path.
- **Green** is considered the color of healing, teaching, endurance, firmness, growth, and good self-esteem. It can mean advances in education, culture, and physical goals.
- **Yellow** is the color of the spontaneous person. It casts warmth, variability, originality, and exhilaration. Yellows, in different shades, can represent different sides of the intellect, from the craftiness of a mustard yellow to the high thoughts of golden yellow. People with yellow surrounding them attract others who are drawn to their inner radiance.
- **Orange** is considered the creative and artistic aura. It represents energy and perception. New ideas can be put into action if people with abundant orange in their auras work on creative projects.
- **Red** is full of passion, hard work, and the desire for achievement. It indicates the drive to live life intensely.

AURAS AND EPILEPSY

Another type of aura may be linked directly to the brain. Some epileptics, including Russian writer Fyodor Dostoyevsky, experience what are called "ecstatic auras" that included bright lights.

He considered the sensations accompanying an epileptic seizure so valuable that he said of them, "In these five seconds I live a lifetime, and for them I shall give away my whole life because it is worth it."

Some researchers believe that Joan of Arc experienced epilepsy, accompanied by ecstatic auras, and visions. Lydia Bayne, M.D., assistant professor of neurology at the University of California, San Francisco, has argued that evidence uncovered by writer Elizabeth Foot-Smith indicates that Joan of Arc suffered from a form of epilepsy called complex partial seizures.

Bayne says not all types of epileptic seizures are convulsions, but are slightly altered states of consciousness, often preceded by an aura. She says that in writings about Joan of Arc it tells of spells consisting of a dream-like state, visions of angels and voices with a messianic message—typical of complex partial seizures.

Not all people, though, find epilepsy joyous. Some who suffer from the condition may have continual seizures throughout the day and not be able to live a normal life. Seizures can damage the organs, such as the heart.

Epilepsy is linked to defects in neurotransmission (or electrical) activity in the brain, with certain amino acids, which are the building blocks of protein, playing a role in the defects. Seizures are the result of an abnormal spread of this electrical activity that travels to other parts of the body through the vagus nerve, which is part of the autonomic nervous system. It has branches to the head, neck, chest, and abdomen area. The vagus nerve functions as a two-way communication link between the brain and other body organs, such as the heart, lungs, and digestive tract—all of which are affected during a seizure.

A new device is under study that may alter certain brain activity to prevent partial seizures, one of two main categories of seizures in adults. Both types of seizures originate in different parts of the brain.

It is the partial seizure most closely associated with auras. They serve as a warning of an impending seizure, according to Richard E. George, M.D., assistant professor of neurosurgery at Baylor College of Medicine.

The partial seizure is called that because it arises from within one area of the brain and gradually spreads to surrounding areas of the brain, rather than affecting the entire brain at the onset.

Those with a partial seizure experience an aura that tips them off to an impending full-blown seizure. During this preseizure, in addition to an aura, they may experience smells, déjà vu or other psychic phenomenon. A young child may become fearful for no reason and run to his or her parents. George classifies this preseizure as a seizure with psychic manifestations.

The new device aborts the spread of the electrical activity and prevents a full complex seizure since it is activated during this auric warning period. "If you desynchronize the electrical activity of the brain, you may prevent the seizure from spreading," says George.

Some patients can be provoked to have seizures by flashing bright lights, but the seizures themselves are electrical activity in the brain.

If the seizures arise from the occipital lobes at the back of the brain, they can produce visual flashing lights, and color. The occipital lobes are involved in the perception of color.

AURAS AND
MIGRAINE HEADACHES

Auras are sometimes experienced by people who suffer from migraine headaches. Some research indicates that the pineal gland, the small, pine-cone shaped organ located above and behind the eyes, may serve as a breeding ground for migraine headaches, according to Joseph U. Toglia, M.D., of Temple University.

Other studies reported in the *American Journal of Epidemiology* show that women with relatively low levels of estrogen may be at increased risk of migraine attacks. The research also shows that while migraines with and without auras may not be distinct diagnostic entities, migraines with auras may simply have a strong genetic association. Evidence from previous studies has shown an association between headaches and various phases of the menstrual cycle. Some clinical studies show that taking estradiol prevents migraine headaches during the menstrual period.

COLORED LIGHT TECHNOLOGY

Another type of aura can be achieved through mind simulation via technology. It's a blend of medical science and Space Age technology tinged with New Age guruism and techno-speculation that promises everything from increased intelligence to help for epileptic patients.

Called "mind machines" "brain turbochargers," "synchroenergizers," or "transcerebral electrostimulation," they blip and bleep in hospitals and the research lab, in walk-in mind gyms, and the home.

It's instant altered states of mind, or advanced medical technology, and some of its biggest boosters have pedigreed medical credentials, while others flirt with new technology by popping into the country's forty or so mind gyms, mostly located in New York and California, for a quick fix of Nirvana. Or they're buying their own mini-mind manipulators to help them rev up or down at home.

These transformational electronic devices used by the layperson include electrostimulators that send small amounts of electricity to the brain to facilitate various states of consciousness, tapes or tones that elicit certain repetitive sound frequencies that synchronize both hemispheres of the brain, and pulsing colored light stimulation to alter moods. Requirements include special headphones and eyeglasses with a control to synchronize it all.

It's believed by a growing number of medical professionals and laypeople alike that the machines offer a buzz to higher consciousness, deep meditations, increased learning capabilities, and control of some diseases and prevention of others. Among the more sophisticated machines, usually found at medical universities, one can view the brain in action.

Achieving altered states, of course, is not new territory. Meditation has been practiced in various cultures for centuries, and can release tension, rejuvenate mental and physical energy, and create spiritual growth.

It is in the area of spiritual growth that causes the most consternation among those who believe that "true" meditation is a difficult task requiring discipline and time for growth or mind expansion.

In other words, and as numerous philosophers and spiritual leaders have said in a variety of ways, "The journey is part of the process and more significant than the destination."

The Ven Dr. Havanpola Ratanasara, head of the Buddhist Sangha Council of Southern California, says, "When you are trying to deal with the mind, and you lack the discipline and commitment that goes with the lifetime journey of meditation, it can be very difficult. It can, instead, attack the mind, which is associated with the brain. The machines deal only with the brain."

"Our minds involve what Americans call 'the soul,' " Ratanasara says. "When a person gets a jolt from the machines, he or she might feel renewed for a short time, but once a person has mastered real meditation, his or her spirit is renewed all the time. Machines don't help the mind develop on a lasting level."

Stimulation from the machines may create a sense of temporary happiness, but not that achieved by yogis or practitioners of Zen Buddhism, which teaches a person how to deal with the pain of life through meditation.

Yet, some believe the devices are okay to use for the fun of it, or for medical purposes, but not for achieving higher spiritual states.

Medical professionals like Alan Paul Brauer, M.D., agree. As director of the Brauer Medical Center in Palo Alto, California, and clinical assistant professor, Department of Psychiatry and Behavioral Sciences at Stanford University, Brauer believes so-called mind machines are best left to the medical field from whence they came.

Brauer's chief interest in the brain machines involves the use of cranial electrostimulation (CES) for the treatment of substance abuse. The technology itself isn't new. CES, which puts a mild jolt of current from one ear lobe to another, has been used for about thirty years in the United States and Europe to help people get to sleep. It gained increased notoriety a few years ago when Scottish physician Meg Patterson used it to help Pete Townsend and Eric Clapton kick their drug addictions.

But today's CES is likely to be hooked up to an electroencephalogram (EEG) that not only provides diagrams of brain waves, but produces color pictures of the brain in action, allowing scientists to witness the neurochemical changes going on.

At the University of California, Los Angeles, Sepulveda Medical Center, under the guidance of Barry Sterman, M.D., a pioneer in mind-control for epileptic patients, sophisticated EEG's, paired with computer screens, pinpoint portions of the brain responsible for seizures. The brain is mapped, producing a template of seizure patterns, and the patient learns to master the unwanted brain patterns during the brief warning period just prior to seizure.

The new machines are a far cry from the strobe lighting used at the turn of the century to elicit peaceful states of mind. Their introduction is attributed to European scientists who cut holes in pieces of circular paper and placed kerosene lights in back of them to produce flashes of light and color into the patient's eyes. The remedy was thought to reduce hysteria in psychiatric patients.

As Tom Budzynski, behavioral medicine coordinator at St. Lukes Hospital in Bellevue, Washington, explains it, "The right research has been going on for a number of years, and some experimentation with a variety of machines had taken place. And recently all of a sudden it began to blossom because the right zeitgeist or spirit of the times appeared and enough people had heard about the process to want to explore further."

This spirit includes the desire to take care of oneself; to mind explore without the use of drugs; less resistance to tapping into altered states of mind; advances in technology; and an opening up to new ideas by the established medical community who were dragged, sometimes kicking and screaming, into an holistic approach to health.

Advances in technology allowed scientists to document "feel good" or altered states brought about by chemical changes in the brain, notably increased levels of endorphins that produce such feelings as "joggers high," or possibly, the "aura state" experienced by some epileptics just before a seizure.

So while controversy surrounds the use of the machines for enlightenment, medical science is interested in them for different purposes.

For example, Chris Newman of Lexicor Medical Technology Inc. in Boulder, Colorado, calls that company's "Neurosearch-24," which is in use at Loma Linda University Medical Center in California to determine the cause of spontaneous remission in some cancer patients, a "quantitative" neurophysiological EEG that measures brain electrical activity across twenty electrodes."

Translated, it means that Neurosearch-24 and similar machines create a picture of "hot" spots in a person's brain by showing what portion of gray matter is being used and, possibly, for what purpose, since it's believed that some cancer patients trigger remission by altering brain states. So if they are able to induce a spontaneous remission, what part of the brain did they use? And can medical therapists train others to use that same part of the brain to promote a similar remission? Tracy Covington, clinical psychologist and researcher at Loma Linda, says they've used similar techniques with chronic pain sufferers, whom they train to stimulate the pain reduction area of the brain.

Making this type of "template" or map of the brain to pinpoint specific areas for others to mimic, is also used to map the brains of creative people while they work so investigators can determine what their brains have in common, and are they working through altered states?

Altered states are linked to hertz (Hz) fluctuations. The four most recognizable states are "beta" which is the everyday brain functioning state that operates at 13 or more cycles (or Hz) per second; "alpha" at 8-13 Hz, which is still alert but more relaxed; "theta," a deep intuitive state that operates from 4 to 7 Hz; and the sleeping state, delta, which waves in from 0 to 4 Hz.

Many scientists also talk about hyper-alert or other mind states that unite the Hz waves of the right and left hemispheres of the brain.

"Certain frequencies are associated with enhanced relaxation or enhanced concentration. That's where super learning comes from. In a more relaxed state one can learn more effectively," says Brauer.

Studies show that the right hemisphere of the brain—the more creative side—shuts down in times of stress.

"It's very sequential. If you are in a stressful situation, you are processing how to get out of it, step by step. And that requires left-brain thinking," says David Siever, president of Comtronic Devices in Alberta, Canada.

So while the left side of the brain does double duty for the out-of-commission right side, which controls the left side of the body (and vice versa), the body sometimes goes amok on the left side. Hence, more musculoskeletal problems on the left side of the body.

Siever's "Comptronic" devices have been used to reduce stress by the University of Alberta Dentistry Department where it was discovered that most patients suffering from temporomandibular joint (TMJ) dysfunction were afflicted on the left side of their faces.

"It's all caused because the right brain gets shut down creating muscular tension that shows up on the left side," says Siever, whose background lies in telecommunications, biofeedback, and physiology. "These machines get the right side going again working in conjunction with the left side. Basically, people on the machines are able to go into what is called 'passive awareness', which is identical to what Zen

masters go into after ten years or so of meditation practice—
only we can do it in twenty to thirty minutes on the
machines," claims Siever, whose devices are touted as the
most powerful and versatile portables on the market.

The effect isn't permanent, however. It simply becomes
easier to slip into a meditative state with continued use of the
machine, or by training oneself to achieve an altered state with
ease after the training. What patients, or those who buy the
machines for home use, or entrepreneurs who establish mind
gyms do, is take the work out of slipping into these various altered
states of mind, and flashing colors are part of this stimulation.

While some believe the "quick fix" approach to altered
states eliminates the discipline required for true
enlightenment, others contend most people don't have the
time to spend years in meditation to accomplish the same
thing. Besides, they say, all aren't seeking enlightenment, they
just want to reduce stress.

Keith Merriman, spokesman for Altered States in Los
Angeles, a pioneer in the mind-gym industry, says mind gyms
promise to be in the 1990s what health spas were to the
1980s with stress reduction as the key motivating factor.

Because stress reduction has become a national
obsession in Japan, the Japanese have latched onto the new
technology. Several mind-spa centers have opened in Tokyo
the last few years according to Merriman.

"What the mind gym offers is a solution—a
technological solution to a problem that is inherent in their
society and ours," he says, adding that whatever else the
machines can do, everyone agrees that they do reduce stress,
and that stress reduction is linked to enhanced creativity,
learning, success building, and self-esteem.

Remove the stress and a poor math learner might
become better. By carrying the stress concept a step further,

it's not unlikely that other brain alterations might improve math learning ability.

"The theory is that good math students use a certain part of the brain more than poor students do, and we'd like to find out if that's true," says Budzynski. And, if true, as researchers suspect, they want to know what portion of the brain is active in the good students, and then teach poor students to activate that part of the brain.

The machines, then, have a growing list of adherents, as well as the possibility of many different types of use. What then, triggers so much controversy?

Attorney and mediator Joel Edelman of Santa Monica is familiar with long-term meditation and the mind machines and says that the controversy surrounding the issue is proof that something phenomenal exists in the machines, but because they explore new territory it brings out the fear in people.

"It's like somebody inventing a new path to Mt. Everest. Reality is the biggest threat to most people, whereas, the biggest threat should be whether the machines work or not (or whether the new path is just as good or better than the old one). They are beneficial if they are beneficial."

Speaking as a mediator, Edelman says he's not for or against the things. "They may benefit one person but not another."

Too, the center of the controversy could be plain resentment, which he likens to a person who attends school for ten years to obtain a certain degree. "Then they meet someone who has acquired the same degree in six months. They're resentful."

Another type of fear is held by some scientists who believe that if the new technology is exploited and trivialized as only a "quick fix," it will become just another fad.

Researchers like Siever feel use of the machines by a layperson is okay, but he hopes the devices will stay primarily in the hands of the medical establishment in order to foster continued research. He believes that pharmaceutical companies will eventually get into mind-machine technology since it can replace many of the mind-altering drugs now in use.

Lynn Henriksen, cofounder of the nonprofit Neurotechnologies Research Institute in Sausalito, California, which serves as a sort of clearinghouse/research center for an array of the devices, said that a foreign reporter told her recently that some nightclubs in London have installed the mind-expanding machines for customers.

Medical researchers take a big "gulp" when they hear stories like that. "I hope this industry will police itself and that people will use good common sense. It's like anything else, it can be overused, and used in combination with drugs and alcohol, it can be abused. It's not like a Nautilus machine. You can get down into altered states and get into something you don't want to," Henriksen cautions.

The center makes no endorsements for any of the thirty or so companies manufacturing the devices, and boasts some of the top mind-machine researchers in the country on its board of directors. These include Stephen LaBerge of Stanford, who is one of the leading authorities in the field of dream states; Robert J. Cosgrove, M.D., an authority in pharmaceutics and biomedical engineering; Lester Fehmi, director of the Princeton Behavioral Medicine and Biofeedback Clinic; and others.

Henriksen says she receives calls of inquiry from Australia, Japan, Germany, England and a few from South Africa, Johannesburg, and the Republic of Singapore. "There's already lots going on in Canada," she says. Some of the inquiries have been from people interested in opening mind gyms, such as two women from Holland who want to use it in their healing work.

Clearly, the machines offer a plethora of uses, and their sophistication depends largely on the price tag, which ranges from $300 to $1,200 for home models, and from $7,000 to $70,000 at medical institutions, or in a few instances, at mind gyms. Most of the machines were more than double that amount only five years ago, so price is a factor in their growing popularity just as it was with the computer revolution. Like the computer, tapping into a potential wonderland with the flick of a switch holds a lure that's not likely to go away.

Yet, strictly as a transformational tool, they're not a lure for everyone. Wendy Nakao (Egyoku), chief administrator of the Zen Center of Los Angeles, says meditation isn't about blissing out. "It's about living in the thick of it. It's about your life. No matter what a machine does, we still have to live our lives. Meditation isn't about getting to any particular altered state. It's about examining the nature of life and death."

Thus far, adherents of mind machines with their flashing colors haven't claimed anything so lofty.

Auras, then, are not only the purview of mystics, but find their place in medical phenomenon. Whatever the cause, both mystically and scientifically, something is occurring in the brain of the person to whom it happens. Medical science has its explanation. Perhaps someday, the theories for why certain people are able to see them will become as clear as some of the auras themselves.

CHAPTER 3

The Power in Color

The use of color in a person's life can take many forms, such as by burning colored candles, by placing colored oils on certain parts of the body, through an appreciation of flowers, and in the use of gems and crystals.

Although these practices vary from one another, they are all linked by a connection with color. It may be that the doing, or the observation of these practices increases awareness, or heightens energy, or simply puts practitioners at ease with themselves and their thoughts. But the practices are used by people throughout the world, and offer a universal connection to the power of color.

CANDLE POWER

The use of candles to elicit certain moods, to bring good luck, as a curative, and as a charm dates back to prehistoric times. Modern use encompasses traditions borrowed from Wicca, black magic, Christianity, Jungian psychology, folklore from societies throughout the world, and ancient mythologies.

Candles are made from wax, paraffin, or tallow. Beeswax is preferred by many practitioners, but most candles today are manmade from esters, alcohol, fatty acids, and solid hydrocarbons. Paraffin used for candles is a product of petroleum. Tallow for candles is usually derived from animal fats, but vegetables also produce tallow.

The candles on the altars of many churches and cathedrals in the world are said to represent the spiritual sense centers of the world, according to Manly Hall, author in 1929 of *The Occult Anatomy of Man*. Candles have a hallowed place in many religions.

Some traditions have been passed down through generations of families and, although they may derive from a single source, each family puts its own individual stamp on the practice. Such traditions can be likened to certain rituals practiced by Native Americans. A tribal practice may take on variations by a family, or an individual. Yet, universal threads, or smoke, trail through most of them.

Californian Donna Caltrider, former history and English literature teacher, who also taught pre-Christian history, gives the example of Wicca practices stemming from a singular source. Within that singular source, individuals may vary the practices by using their family's "Book of Shadows," written by and updated by the practitioner.

Much of the popular use of candles in Western culture today is due to the Wicca movement, but Caltrider says recent candle popularity can also be traced to the First World War when candles were placed in windows to protect loved ones overseas. The interest in candles also received a boost in the 1960s from the hippies.

Caltrider believes that the symbolic use of candles puts people in touch with themselves, and helps them deal with the emotions involved with problems in their lives. It also relieves anxiety.

One of the best examples she gives is taken from a true life experience. Her mother, now deceased, had been physically attacked in her home. Caltrider arranged a grouping of candles for her mother to view during her convalescence. "She got to where she would say, 'Hey, the candles are going out.' They became a symbol of security for her while she recuperated from the trauma. It was like watching fish in an aquarium. Watching the fish mellows a person out. You get to know when the fish have high energy or low energy. It gives you time to think. She would just sit there and watch the candles. It was inexpensive psychological counseling."

Caltrider acknowledges that many people who burn candles add a lot of symbolism to the practice, such as burning certain candles, or gathering materials to be used with the candle rituals during certain phases of the moon. And she says it's fine for them, but that it doesn't negate more simple practices.

"Most every church in the world uses candles, and it goes back to early pagan religions, and even further back to gods and goddesses of fire. We had goddesses of the hearth, or of the entire city. I think probably it goes back to the time when man first developed fire. 'Hey, this is good stuff,' they may have said."

Caltrider, who has been involved with metaphysical practices for more than forty years, and who is considered an authority on the use of candles, incorporates many ancient practices into her candle burning rituals.

Following are a few of her personal rituals with explanations:

- Beeswax candles are preferable to tallow candles, which are made from animal fat. This preference may be the result of early use of beeswax by royalty or the wealthy, as opposed to the tallow candles used by the poor.
- Select solid color candles, and not ones that are one color on the outside and another inside.
- Always burn at least one separate white candle with the colored candle of choice. This is done to keep the thoughts pure. Caltrider burns white candles on either side of the colored candle, and sometimes adds additional white candles to represent the four corners of the earth. She also uses a little salt or earth, and water so that the four elements are represented: earth, air, fire (the candles), and water.
- Never ask for something that is going to hurt someone else. Many candle practitioners believe that if such a request is made, it will circle back and harm the candle burner at least threefold.
- Use common sense when burning candles instead of following dogma. A good example of dogma is the age-old belief that once a candle is lit, it has to burn out by itself. "I may have believed that prior to the earthquakes that struck Big Bear, where I live. But if I've lit a candle and then have to go somewhere, I always put it out—not by blowing, but with a candle snuffer. Leaving a candle to tip over in an earthquake and burn down the house just doesn't make much sense," she says. "My feeling is that the power of the candle keeps going even though it isn't burning."
- You can put an inscription on the bottom of the candle. "If I were trying to draw someone to me, I would write his name on the bottom of a pink candle for love. Or if

someone owed me money, and I needed it, I might inscribe 'money' on the bottom of the candle."

- You can also make up your own chant. Some people use established chants from books, or those they learn from others, but Caltrider uses her own, such as, "Please watch over my home (give the address or location), guard and protect it."

In terms of the colors of candles and their significance, Caltrider offers the following interpretations:

- **Purple** candles are sometimes used in connection with the white ones for added spirituality since purple is symbolic of spirituality and royalty. "Purple is heavy duty spiritualism," she says.
- **Red** is the symbol of super-high-powered energy. But you have to be careful, because if someone who is already angry comes into a room with a red candle, it can heighten the anger. Or if you're depressed and burn a red candle to give you energy, it may worsen the present condition.
- **White**, of course, is for purity. Thoughts must be pure and distinct before a certain candle is burned. If you want to learn to like someone you dislike, it's not good enough to say, "I want to learn to like this person even though he or she is a jerk." The thought has to be pure—"I want to like so and so, period." The person burning the candle must have already worked through his or her dislike of the person based on assumptions about that person.
- **Pink** is symbol of love. "I would burn red and pink and white together. Red is also lust, and I see nothing wrong with that. A little lust never hurt anyone," she says.

- **Green** is for new beginnings. Think of it as the color of spring, when things begin anew. So green can stand for increased wealth, more vigor, feeling good. It's a healing color. "If I want to feel mentally invigorated, then probably I would go into green and, of course, always with the white."
- **Brown** is for depression. "There are times when you need to deal with depression. I would start with white, and then burn brown." Or she might burn gray, which is a neutral color. By burning these color, an individual acknowledges he or she is depressed, which can be a first step to recovery. By burning the candle, the person is doing something positive about it—something concrete.
- **Yellow** is very good for maintaining friendship. "I've used it when a close friend is moving. Or you may want to keep a group of people together, and you burn a candle for each of them at the same time."
- **Orange** can be a positive color. It can be used in place of red for energy and vigor. Caltrider has used it for healing.
- **Blue**, like white is a purification color. It is considered a candle of mood alteration towards a more mellow state. If you're agitated, a blue candle might help.
- **Black** candles have gotten a bad rap. It's true they can be used for negative energy, and a person has to be careful using them. But black candles can also be used in some setups for healing and to dissipate negative energy, according to Caltrider. "You're asking it to absorb all the negativity surrounding you or another person."

People using black candles need to be in touch with themselves, and know where they are coming from. All thoughts of negativity have to be eliminated before working with black candles.

When Caltrider uses a black candle, which is infrequently, she surrounds it with five white ones—one in each corner with the two at the bottom set closer to the black candle. A white candle is also placed above, and in line with the black one. Sitting between the two white candle in back is a small mound of salt to the left, a container of water in the middle and a small mound of dirt to the right of the water, representing three of the earth's elements. The candle represents air and fire.

FLOWER POWER

Ancient and medieval lore have sprinkled American culture with the symbolism of flowers.

Florist Grace Atwood says much of the lore comes from medieval times when knights honored certain floral customs.

Yellow was a sign of jealousy, red signified love, white purity. "If a knight sent a yellow and white rose he was saying he was in love but also jealous."

Yet, each age develops its own flower power.

"Today, people are living such structured lives that they want something in flowers that helps them relax, that is going to tweak their minds and maybe transport them, even for a brief moment, into nature." Along with this idea, comes the current trend for less structured floral arrangements in a variety of nontraditional colors, and the use of nontraditional flowers.

"My daughter, for instance, likes daisies because it reminds her of freedom," says Atwood, pointing to white daisies growing in her yard.

Atwood believes people are initially drawn to flowers because they take away the sterility of life. "The inner self knows about these things that the outside person may not be attuned to. So we are drawn to certain colored flowers without consciously knowing why."

Flowers are also good teachers, she says, citing a class she taught on aging using a deep red rose bud yet to unfold, a fully blooming rose slightly lighter of the same base color, and finally the rose in a wilted stage—faded, but still beautiful.

Paula Wade, florist and owner of "The Little Green House" in Big Bear Lake, also believes that as a flower fades, it holds its own sort of beauty. Flowers stay on her desk until the leaves fall, because she sees beauty in their change.

"People have had so many manmade things in their lives that they like the change from life to withered. You can witness this change with flowers," she says. "Man can color something any shade today, but when God does it, it's awesome."

The awe for flowers, though, isn't new. William Wilberforce, English statesman, wrote in the eighteenth century: "Flowers are God's thoughts of beauty taking form to gladden mortal gaze."

Another effect of the times in which we live is the trend toward flowers in the primary colors all blended together. "People still like pink and white, and other traditional gift flower colors, but more are reaching out to the variety of colors offered today," says Wade.

These colors in flowers reflect the similar attitude in clothing that is brighter, more mixed, and which borrows from several cultures intermingling. Many of the flowers sold today in the United States come from countries like Japan, Colombia, and Holland—cultures with a different color sense. Growers are also developing different colored strains of flowers to accommodate the new tastes in flowers.

Growers throughout the world have taken note with increased efforts to produce cut and garden flowers in new and bright colors. Names like "Raspberry Ripple" (De Vroomen Holland) and "Accent Burgundy Star" (Goldsmith Seeds, Inc.) and "Peacock Mix" (W. Atlee Burpee & Co.) speak for themselves.

"The how and why of new colors is limited only by the current technology," says Marvin N. Miller, market research manager for Geo. J. Ball, Inc.

With biotechnology—gene manipulation—more colors, delivered at a faster pace are on the horizon. As it stands now, generating new colors involves a lot of chance. "We do a lot of crosses, and we don't know until afterwards what we're going to get out of it. When you cross two things, in traditional breeding, a lot happens, and you can't control most of it. When you cross two things, just like with people, you get some attributes from both parents, and you don't always know which ones you'll get until afterward. Then if you like it, you can keep producing that seed. But when you cross the two parents, you might end up getting all red, or mostly white, or you might get different heights other than what you were after."

The potential for biotech is that growers will be able to control specific genes, and not have to go through such a chancy prospect.

Still, biotech won't introduce any colors that haven't been grown somewhere, at sometime, even though no humans may have ever seen them. The plants may carry many different genes, but they've been around for a long time, manipulating and changing themselves.

Red, though, still remains the most popular color in flowers. Miller talks about roses (cut), geraniums (outside) and poinsettias (potted). Historically, red roses accounted for 90 percent of stemmed roses bought. But that has dropped to about 70 percent in the past few years. Miller attributes it to women buying more roses. Men prefer red, women like yellow. Poinsettias, too, do well in red, even though it has dipped from about 90 percent ten years ago to between 60 to 80 percent. Geraniums held at 85 percent red, but have gone as low as 50 percent in recent years.

"Red still dominates in those three crops, but the percentage has declined," says Miller. "Pinks and whites have taken up the slack."

Miller attributes part of the trend to women's increased earning power. "They're earning their own salaries, and buy flowers on impulse at the supermarkets. In terms of geraniums, that's the case as well. Women are making more decisions on what they are buying for the garden and patio, and in that respect, we're getting more diversity."

Another part of the trend may be due to baby boomers. "They're more interested in new colors and aren't tied to tradition. It isn't that they want to break with tradition. They may not be aware of the traditions," says Miller.

Another major change is that men have become much more flower conscious, both in buying, and receiving them. Football player Merle Olson's television commercials for FTD, has opened the door for men, according to Wade. Men have a great influence on the flower industry now, and they like bold, bright colors.

A survey commissioned by the American Floral Marketing Council in 1993 found that over half of the men surveyed said they had received flowers from their sweethearts.

Flowers, according to 95 percent of those surveyed, continue to be a universal sign of romance. "Color is one of the most subtle, yet stimulating and manipulating concepts we have," says Wade. "And it's all there in flowers."

The American Floral Marketing Council offers these tips for handling cut flowers:

- If a commercial floral preservative isn't used, change the water daily.
- Add warm water daily to the arrangement if a preservative is used.
- If the flowers arrive in a bouquet or wrapped box, store them in a cool place until they can be placed in a water-filled container.
- For loose flowers, recut the stems with a sharp knife. Do this under water so the stem will draw in water instead of air.
- Place flowers in warm water immediately after cutting, and make certain the container is clean.
- Strip off leaves under the water line of the container. Leaves in water promote bacterial growth.
- If the water becomes cloudy, replace it immediately.
- Place vases in a cool spot, away from direct sunlight and heating or cooling vents. Appliances such as television give off heat, so don't sit flowers on them.
- If the flowers wilt, fill the sink with warm water, recut the stems under water and submerge the flowers for about forty-five minutes. Replace them in container with fresh water.

FLOWER REMEDIES

"Any plant evokes a certain color coordination," says Thor Kaslof of Ellon (Bach USA) Inc., distributors of Bach flower remedies. Bach was a London physician who developed natural remedies that relied on the medicinal power of the essences of flowers. He claimed certain flowers had an energy wavelength in tune with the human energy field. "Since color therapy is vibrational medicine, it is believed to be related to Bach's work," says Kaslof.

Bach claimed that each of his select group of thirty-eight flowers contained energy wavelengths in tune with certain frequencies in the human energy field. Interruptions such as stress, could distort the human energy field, making a person vulnerable to disease. The energy of the flowers could rebalance the distortion, he claimed.

Bach solarized flower heads in spring water, and then added alcohol as a preservative, a method that is similar to the Hindu use of solarized water for healing, although no flowers are used. The Hindu patient, though, drinks the water, *sans* alcohol.

PYRAMID POWER

For more than 100,000 years, various civilizations throughout the world worshipped the sun. Ancient civilizations, based in Egypt, used the sun's rays in prism effects to produce colors for healing, enlightenment, mood changes, and worship.

Roland Hunt writes in *Lighting Therapy and Color Harmony* that the Great Pyramid of Giza at one time held the secrets of the ancient wisdom of color, and is, in fact, itself designed as a prism.

Because of that influence, many of the ancient lamps designed to trap the sun's rays to produce color for ritual use, were designed like pyramids. Later electric lamps used in color therapy followed much the same design.

GEM AND CRYSTAL POWER

Gems and crystals have been used for centuries for healing and other attainments. Such use is found in records dating back to 400 B.C. The significance of certain gems though, takes us back to prehistorical times. Perhaps the oldest use of modern man's knowledge of certain gems in ritual dates back more than a million years.

In one of the geological digs at Olduvai Gorge, in Tanzania, eventually made famous by Louis and Mary Leakey, fragments of red ochre or iron oxide (moonstone), not native to the area were found among some crude stone tools.

And at a younger dig at the Terra Amata cave in Southern France where early man nested about three hundred thousand years ago, pieces of ochre have also been found. Described as pencil-shaped, and varying in color from yellow to purple, it is believed they were used as colored crayons, and as a source of pigment.

To fashion such materials required heating and firing to particular temperatures to produce color changes, and pounding the ore into tiny flakes to be mixed with coloring agents such as urine, plant juices, water, and blood.

It is speculated that these early people used the resulting crayons or paste to decorate the body, or to be used in certain rituals, much as it is still used in some tribal societies.

The use of red ochre in ritual may be linked to early man and woman's identification with the mysterious and transforming quality of blood.

According to Lyall Watson, author of *Lightning Bird*, an Australian aboriginal legend tells that red ochre deposits were formed from the blood flow of Unthippa women. Certain sacred ochre sites in Australia may only be mined by revered old men of the tribe.

Watson concludes that throughout history, men and women have been attracted to colored iron ores, and in particular to red ochre, because it looks like and has become symbolic of blood.

Many cultures use the red of ochre in burial ceremonies, and to decorate themselves and the deceased with red ochre or bloodstone.

Thus, since primeval times, colored gems have held special significance to men and women.

ANCIENT USE OF GEMS FOR HEALING

Many societies today still use some of the ancient remedies associated with gems. Practitioners in the United States often tape a particular gem to a sore spot, or a place they wish to heal, such as a small rose quartz taped to the heart area for healing a broken heart. Some common uses of gems include:

- Amber for fever, rheumatism, toothache, headache.
- Amethyst for gout.
- Carnelian for hemorrhage.
- Chalcedony for gallstones.
- Emerald for eye diseases, and poison antidote.
- Jade for easing childbirth.
- Jet for epilepsy.
- Malachite for sore muscles.

CRYSTALS FOR HEALING

Crystal is clear, transparent quartz. It is also a solidified form of a substance in which the atoms or molecules are arranged in a definite pattern that is repeated regularly in three dimensions. Many of the colored crystals used in healing are colored varieties classed as semiprecious-precious stones.

The use of crystals for a variety of purposes has been on a steady increase for the past twenty years, and practices of old have been transformed into rituals that address current lives and issues.

Similar to candle rituals, crystal use also draws upon a variety of group, family, and individual practices, although basic rituals lie at the core.

Lisa Mobius, California artist, learned the basics of crystal power from a practitioner in Long Beach. She later added to her knowledge from metaphysicians in New Mexico, and then in Europe and the Mideast where she traveled and worked.

She uses crystals throughout her day as a matter of routine, but also practices special rituals, and has worked helping others regain balance in matters concerned with daily living. Like Caltrider's advice for candles, Mobius is practical and not dogmatic about her use of crystals.

She suggests that a person take his or her time selecting a crystal. It should "twinkle" at the person. Then hold the crystal and make certain it feels comfortable, and compatible.

Before an individual uses that crystal, it should be washed with soap and water, and then ritually cleansed. Her preference is to dip it in ocean water, but oil from the hyssop seed is powerful. The crystal can also be immersed in Kosher salt, or sea salt.

Following that procedure, the crystal can be placed in the sun for several hours, or added to a crystal cluster to empower it.

If the crystal has been touched by someone else, especially if the person has brought negative energy into the home, that crystal can be empowered again by placing it within four double-terminated crystals, or ritually cleansing it again.

Each crystal has a terminus, or point within it. Some have two and provide this double termination.

Before programming a crystal it must be deprogrammed if it has been touched by someone else. To deprogram:

1. Place the termination point between the palms of the hand, termination end down toward the earth, and rub it as if you are creating friction to warm your hands.
2. Then rotate the crystal counter-clockwise three times, keeping the termination down toward the earth.
3. Turn the termination point upward and shake the crystal down like you would a thermometer.
4. Next, rotate the crystal clockwise three times, and when you think about what you want the crystal to do for you, clutch it in the palm of your hand with the fingers wrapped around it, and blow "the breath of life into the crystal."

She cautions that this deprogramming, and incantation procedure should never be done by a person who is tense or angry. Mobius uses the crystals in a variety of ways:

- To bring something into your life, such as energy, a new job, or new awareness, proceed with the routines or incantations on any day following the first day of a new moon until the third day of the full moon.
- If you program the crystal to get rid of things, such as a smoking habit, a boyfriend or girlfriend, follow the same procedure.

Requests are written out, and then said aloud as you go through the procedure.

Colored crystals can be used, but Mobius prefers the clear variety, and then she envisions the color associated with whatever she is requesting.

For example, if she is requesting a healing, she envisions the crystal surrounded by green, layered by pink over the green. Green is a healing color, and pink adds love. Basic colors one might want to use are:

- Green for healing.
- Yellow for cleansing.
- Red for energy.
- Blue for calming.
- Orange for increasing emotions and creativity.
- Pink for love.

Through envisioning, some practitioners place themselves within the crystal. To do so, one must first draw on the power of the white light used in meditation for protection, and make certain you have a feeling of being grounded.

To perform a ritual on another person, Mobius has the person lie down on a table or bench, but not on the floor, head pointing north. Colored lights, designating the purpose of the ritual, are placed about a foot away from the head and feet of the person. Mobius adds soft background music. Crystals are placed along the body's chakra points, inside and outside the extremities, accounting for seventeen in all. They are first placed with the terminators pointing to the feet. Mobius then swoops her hands down from the head to the feet rapidly. She does this about three times while she envision the impurities, negative energy, or blockages within the body being washed away.

Once this procedure is completed, place the terminators toward the head of the person and turn out the lights. Sweep the hands in the opposite direction—feet to head. This reestablishes good energy balance, and fills the person with the desired outcome, such as increased creativity, reduction of anxiety, increased strength or other conditions.

Mobius is cautious about misusing crystals. "I once walked into a store and the clerk complained of feeling dizzy and agitated. She was wearing a massive crystal ring, like a cubic zircon. I asked her about the ring and she said it was a display model that she had put on. The ring obviously hadn't been purified, and she wasn't attuned to its powers. Once she took the ring off, she said she felt better.

Another time, a friend had gathered a small bag of crystals from a site in upstate New York. He placed them beneath the driver's seat of the car he was driving and headed home. Needless to say, he drove erratically all the way home.

Mobius offers these additional tips about crystals:

- An amethyst and rose quartz together calms a room.
- Teens in turmoil should wear a rose quartz crystal.
- You can program a crystal to help you remember and then hold it in your hand during a test.
- Wear only natural crystal, not a manmade crystal.
- Always wear a crystal with the terminator down.
- If a stone is lusterless and depleted, renew it by placing it on a crystal cluster.
- Don't wear crystal with metal.

GEMS FOR BALANCE

Certain gems and minerals, considered precious or semiprecious have been used for aligning the body's chakra system (for further reading on chakras, refer to chapter 2). Usually, but not always, the gems mimic the colors of the chakra system. Thus, red gems are used for healing at the base of the spine, and also for anemia, to energize, and to correct poor circulation.

- **First chakra, associated with red:** bloodstone, carnelian, alexandrite, and garnet
- **Second chakra, associated with orange:** wulfenite, citrine, and amber
- **Third chakra:** chrysoberyl, orange citrine, yellow topaz, and calcite
- **Fourth chakra:** peridot, emerald, malachite, jade, and beryl
- **Fifth chakra, blue:** turquoise, sapphire, and aquamarine
- **Sixth chakra, indigo (purple/blue):** sodalite, lapis lazuli, and amethyst
- **Seventh chakra:** clear quartz, diamond, clear agate, and gold and/or white topaz

As well as aligning and balancing the body's chakra system, the gems, like the chakra systems, are associated with particular parts of the body:

- **Orange** gems are used for the lower trunk area covering the spleen and liver, and also to reduce fear, anxiety, and low blood pressure.
- **Yellow** gems are used for distress in the navel area, including the adrenal glands and pancreas, and for stomach distress and depression.
- **Green** gems help vitalize the heart area, and also circulation and ulcers.
- **Blue** gems can have an affect on the throat and thyroid, as well as treating high blood pressure, fevers, tension, and skin eruptions.
- **Indigo** gems, linked to the pituitary gland, are also

used with some mental and nervous disorders.
- **Violet** gems, as well as the white ones, are also linked to the pineal gland and can be used to enhance self-esteem, and a general feeling of calm.

YOUR BIRTHSTONE AND THE ZODIAC

Since ancient times man has been associating certain colored precious and semiprecious stones and gems with different months of the year. The meanings given those stones are often in keeping with the personalities attributed to various Zodiacal signs, which overlap the regular months of the year.

It is believed that the original twelve stones were those worn on the breastplate of Aaron, brother of Moses, depicting the twelve tribes of Israel.

These were later transposed to the Gregorian calendar and their meanings have remained much as they were in medieval times when a person wore a different stone for every month in the hopes of warding off evil spirits. The vibrant colors of these stones have much to do with their magical impunity and even though they have been changed, due to the rarity or abundance of synthetic stones, the colors have generally stayed the same. Also, many of the ancient stones were garnered from the same properties as the more modern ones.

Here then are the monthly meanings of the stones transposed to the Zodiac. The Zodiac signs overlap the birthstone months.

December/January/February:
Capricorn (Dec. 20-Jan. 20), Aquarius (Jan. 21-Feb. 19)
The deep transparent RED GARNET is the birthstone for January and is associated with devotion and

steadiness. This is in keeping with the January Capricorn (the goat), whose people are noted for their quiet way of getting the job done. No fanfare here. They gently plod along and surprise their contemporaries when they end up on top.

January Aquarians, too, fall under the spell of the red garnet. They are the makers of friends and once having done so, are loyal for life, although their friends may never understand them. They never get heavy on intimacy.

February/March:
Pisces (Feb. 20-March 20)

AMETHYST, a purple variety of quartz, is the birthstone of February. It stands for sincerity. The ancient Greeks believed the stone could prevent intoxication.

February Aquarians and Pisces are both sincere in their quest for independence and the fish (Pisces) also searches for perfection.

March/April:
Aries (March 21-April 20)

For the month of March, the BLOODSTONE or AQUAMARINE, both which stand for courage, are the birthstones. The aquamarine is a bluish-green stone, as was the jasper, which was the ancient birthstone for March.

March Pisces (see above) share this birthstone with March Aries people, who have the reputation of being fearless. Their mercurial tempers often hide any fears they might have, which helps make them appear courageous.

Pisces people don't have the temper associated with their neighbor, Aries, because they mask it with idealism. But their view of an ideal world takes a certain amount of courage.

April/May/June:
Taurus (April 21-May 21), Gemini (May 22-June 21)

"Success in love" is promised by the EMERALD birthstone for May. This rich green stone is placed high in value along with the ruby and diamond. In ancient times it was the birthstone for June and the agate was the stone for May.

May Taureans are absolutely romantic. They are staunch in their love, and although they may seem domineering, they're also trustworthy and loyal.

The bull bumps shoulders with May Gemini people. They too find success in love, but not with the staunchness of the Taurean. Their mates must be prepared for the unexpected at all times. Geminis find success in love, but only if they have an understanding mate.

June/July:
Cancer (June 22-July 23)

The PEARL, MOONSTONE, or ALEXANDRITE (which is a deep green stone as was the emerald which formerly belonged to June), are now the birthstones for June. They have as their meaning, health and longevity.

June Geminis (see above) need all the help they can muster regarding health because they suffer minor ills constantly, probably brought about by their restless nature. They share these birthstones with June Cancer people, who are tuned into their own moods to such a degree that it affects their health. Both could use the help of these birthstones to keep them from worrying so much about their health.

July/August:
Leo (July 24-Aug. 23)

July Cancereans (see above) can use the help of the clear, deep red RUBY of July, which is their birthstone because the ruby stands for "contentment," which is elusive to Cancer people.

It's right on target for July Leos, however. Leos are completely happy with themselves because they know they're right. Because of this, they're able to calmly handle any given situation without getting ruffled.

August/September:
Virgo (Aug. 24-Sept. 23)

The SAPPHIRE, a transparent, deep blue precious stone that once belonged to April, is now the birthstone for September. It stands for "clear thinking." The peridot, taken from chrysolite, was the ancient stone for this month. August Virgos can also take advantage of the stability of the sapphire, to add to their calmness.

It also suits the well-balanced personality of September Libras (below) whose forte is the scales of justice.

September/October/November:
Libra (Sept. 24-Oct. 23), Scorpio (Oct. 24-Nov. 22)

October has as its modern stones the OPAL, the TOURMALINE or, more recently, the ROSE ZIRCON. These stones stand for "hope." October's ancient stone was the aquamarine.

October Libras are comfortable with these stones. Possibly no other sign lends itself so well to hope in the relation to the optimistic Libra person.

October Scorpions also share these stones, but are not so well suited to them. They are not so hopeful or optimistic.

November/December:
Sagittarius (Nov. 23-Dec. 21)

December Sagittarians share three shades of blue as their birthstone. They are the LAPIS LAZULI, an azure blue semiprecious stone; the TURQUOISE; and the icy blue ZIRCON. They stand for "prosperity."

If there is anything a November or December Sagittarian strives for, it is accomplishment and success, which are forerunners to prosperity.

December Capricorns (see top of list), like their Sagittarian counterparts, are high achievers. They like to win and tend to be prosperous because of these characteristics.

The beauty and character of each precious or semiprecious stone or gem will always have a marked influence upon the wearer, much as the Sun sign, and people who wear these birthday stones may be enhancing their own unique personalities as divined by the heavenly bodies.

TRADITIONAL BIRTHSTONES

The Jewelry Industry Council lists the following gems for ancient and modern birthstone designations.

MONTH	ANCIENT	MODERN
January	Garnet	Garnet
February	Amethyst	Amethyst
March	Jasper	Bloodstone or Aquamarine
April	Sapphire	Diamond
May	Agate	Emerald
June	Emerald	Pearl, Moonstone or Alexandrite
July	Onyx	Ruby
August	Carnelian	Sardonyx or Peridot
September	Chrysolite	Sapphire
October	Aquamarine	Opal or Tourmaline
November	Topaz	Topaz
December	Ruby	Turquoise or Zircon

A person's personal world is not only powered by color but enhanced by the beauty of the colored objects surrounding the person. Nature provides these colors in abundance from the flowers a person sighs over, to the gems at which he or she marvels. One does not have to combine ritual with the use of this colored bounty. It's there for the asking on a hillside blooming with wildflowers, or a church altar holding a candelabra. Common granite contains a multitude of color if one looks closely enough. Embracing these common treasures is power of itself.

CHAPTER 4

The Color of Your Dreams

Ancient soothsayers and philosophers and modern sleep research scientists alike have puzzled over the meaning and mechanisms of dreams. While some scientists today disdain dream interpretation, others maintain that even with current scientific understanding of what causes dreams, they still convey important meanings to the dreamer.

DO DREAMS HAVE MEANING?

Artists and other creative types, from Robert Louis Stevenson, who based *The Strange Case of Dr. Jekyl and Mr. Hyde* on a dream, to painters, especially the Surrealists of the 1920s, have used their dreams to foster creativity.

The beginnings of religions have also been attributed to efforts to understand and interpret dreams. And Australian Aborigines trace their beginnings to "Dreamtime" or "Sacred Time"—the mythological outpourings of the creation of the things of the earth.

Waud Kracke, associate professor of anthropology at the University of Illinois at Chicago who specializes in the cross-cultural study of dreams, says the Parintintin Indians of Brazil take their dreams seriously.

"Since they have a twelve-hour day and twelve-hour night, they tend to dream more. They go to bed soon after dusk and rise early. During the night they will wake from a dream and go by the fire and, perhaps, tell someone about their dream. They will go back to sleep and dream some more. Maybe they will get up again and tell about it. So they have continuing dreams. They don't just remember the last dream they had like we do because of the way we go to bed and get up at an appointed time. They tend to remember all the dreams they have during various stages of REM [rapid eye movement] sleep."

The visual images that come to people during their sleep cycles may convey many messages. The meanings vary with the dreamer and the society. Obviously, the Brazilian Indians placed great importance on dreams.

Western culture also places importance on dreams, but not in the same manner, or to the degree as the Parintintins.

Current Western theories lean toward the cause being physiological, rather than purely psychological, with the interpretations varying from culture to culture, and individual to individual.

However, one book, *Oneirocritica*, written in the second century A.D. by Artemidorus, a Roman soothsayer, served as the foundation of many other books on dream interpretations up until the beginning of the twentieth century. Psychologists Sigmund Freud and Carl Jung, who embraced the importance of dreams, gave credit to Artemidorus's work.

Sigmund Freud, considered the founder of psychoanalysis, used people's dreams to help them discover hidden feelings. Carl Jung, a Swiss psychologist, who initially followed in Freud's footsteps, eventually developed his own theories involving the feminine and masculine principle in men and women (anima and animus) and a collective unconscious involving symbols referred to as archetypes. He believed these archetypes are often found in dreams.

Several archetypal motifs, such as flying, falling, certain numbers and colors, take on universal meanings, but also have significance to a culture and the individual dreamer. Jung also believed dreams could predict the future. So did Artemidorus. He believed two classes of dreams existed—the somnium, that dealt with the future; and the insomnium, which concerned everyday life.

Jung considered the somnium the "great" dream, according to Norman McKenzie, author of *Dreams and Dreaming*. Jung's great dream consisted of the archetypes or symbolic material, and was loaded with powerful spiritual or mystical effects that were not easily understood by the dreamer.

The actual process of dreaming, though—its physiological cause—didn't become apparent until the middle of the 1950s. Many studies and theories existed on the causes of dreams, but it took modern technology to decipher the dreaming brain, although scientists are still debating exactly what all the findings mean. Yet, the addition of scientific findings do not diminish the dream's importance.

With the advent of studies of the brain's electrical activity, and the discovery of REM and NREM (non-rapid eye movement) in the 1950s, the cause of dreams has itself, become electrically charged. REM sleep lasts less than thirty minutes in about four or five phases during the sleeping night, and is the period when most dreaming occurs. The other time is spent in NREM, *sans* dreams. Birds and nearly all mammals experience REM sleep, including newborn babies. Some studies indicate that a fetus experiences more dream time that it will at any other time in its life outside the womb. Highly stressed individuals, too, seem to increase their dream time.

Also, people with emotional disturbances, or who suffer or have suffered trauma, such as war veterans and victims of child abuse, have recurring dreams and nightmares.

The most popular current theory is that dreams are the result of electrical signals originating in the brain stem that make contact with other parts of the brain that control vision, hearing, movement, and memory centers. By use of positron emission tomography (PET scans) of the brain, researchers have located these areas that appear to be most active during dreaming. Some believe that the limbic brain that activates the emotions, also receives impulses from the brain stem. It is as if the brain's neurons are receiving information from the outside world, but they are not.

It was also discovered that the brain stem contains cells that turn on REM sleep, and others that turn it off.

Since the brain is a chief "sorter" of information, it tries to take all the random information from these disparate parts, stuff it into certain areas, such as the cortex, and come up with an explanation. Because the process lacks outside information, and is given in bits—a bit here, one over there—the message takes on a sort of rambling scenario. It often leaves the awakened dreamer asking, "Now what did all that mean?"

Martin Seligman, professor of psychiatry at the University of Pennsylvania, says that imposing patterns on unpatterned stimuli is the function of dreams. Making order out of chaos is highly innate behavior.

Seligman gives an example of this desire for order: About fifteen years ago during a demonstration at the university another researcher took a string of Christmas light bulbs and crumpled up the string so that they appeared to blink randomly, rather than sequentially. He then played some recorded Beatles music, and the audience perceived that the lights were pulsating in time to the music, although it was actually random. The listeners and viewers of the lights, were imposing patterned material on unpatterned stuff. Humans are creatures of order. It seems to be innate condition to try to make order out of chaos.

Other theories claim that the information contained in a dream is stored information critical to survival. Another maintains that sorting takes place because the brain "dumps" unnecessary information and stores useful information.

None of the theories or discoveries, though, claim that dreaming isn't useful and thought-provoking. They involve life's events and thoughts—perhaps on an unconscious as well as a conscious level, and other levels not yet tapped.

People who claim they don't dream, usually just don't remember, except with certain types of psychosis or other illnesses.

Despite the theories, many scientists and lay people alike believe that dreams have meaning, and reveal truths about ourselves. Leading dream scientist, Allan Hobson, author of The Dreaming Brain, acknowledges that he keeps a dream journal. In one of his recorded dreams he talks about a rich red, gold brocaded frock coat.

DREAMING IN COLOR

People's dreams aren't all in color, according to some researchers who believe that most color-filled dreams probably occur later in the sleep cycle, with those in shades of black and white arriving earlier in the sleeping stages. They believe that about 80 percent of dreams occur in color.

Seligman, though, believes people seldom, if ever, dream in black and white. "Black and white seems to be a photographer's invention. I think it's biologically impossible to dream in black and white, unless, perhaps, the person has severe color blindness," he says.

People who have experience with color, even minimally, incorporate that into their dreams. "I had a patient who was blind from birth who said she dreamed in color. She lost her vision as one of several premature infants who were hyperoxygenated, so maybe she had a very early experience with color before she was treated," he says.

Seligman also offers some insight into the extremely vivid or translucent colors in which humans sometimes dream. "We have very vivid images in dreams, and one of the basic processes in dreams is visual hallucination. The theory of dreaming says that every so often the brain's visual system produces hallucinations. The hallucinations are caused when the brain's emotional process and visual process occur at the same time."

The theory says that visual process during REM sleep has two parts, one of which is a spike or phasic activity. The other is considered the quiescent, or more quiet time. When the spike occurs, everything, including color, is more vivid. And when a person is wakened during this phasic period of REM, he or she is more likely to remember the hallucination, which included the vivid color.

One way to get in touch with your dreams is to keep a dream journal, and to jot down notes, including the colors, immediately upon awakening.

A COLORFUL DREAM

Recounted here is an as-told-to sequence of dreams that is laced with color throughout, and which eventually had great meaning to the dreamer. Consider that the dreamer, in her early forties, was going through a divorce after twenty years of marriage begun at the age of seventeen, was attending college, and had prospects for a great job. Portions have been omitted, but the skeleton of the dream illustrates the importance of color.

It was just before dawn when the journey began, and I was aware of the vibrancy of colors all about—nearly translucent. The green of the trees that surrounded the cold, armor-gray castle where I waited, which was dark, translucent, and still as death. The dark blue cape that covered me from head to toe was rich and deep and provided warmth just by its very lushness.

Two horses approached—one a large sturdy white one of powerful strength and wide rump. It smelled of earth and carried an air of intelligence that made its nostrils flare as if sniffing the aroma of other worlds. The other horse, smaller, though sturdy, with taut muscles skimming over its dark, black body, had dark eyes that danced and teased.

The two horses offered a choice.

The white horse, which was neither male nor female, spoke first, as if ordained that right, and said, "My journey will be slow and full of mystery. It will take you through canyons, up steep mountains, through swamps and into the desert. It may take forever to arrive at your destination and the journey will be rigorous. You will grow weary but wiser."

The black horse dug its right hoof into the ground several times, as if agitated at having to wait for the white one to finish speaking. It seemed, though, in awe of the larger, older horse.

Finished, the white one listened patiently as the black horse urged, "Ride me. I can get you there faster. Hop on. I know shortcuts and the journey will be rapid. You can begin anew when you get there."

I shuddered glancing back at the shadow-filled castle knowing the decision must be made quickly, or else the castle and all its walled protection would reach out and grab me with its tendrils as it had for so long.

A young, nameless girl, a confidant of sorts, assisted me, and urged me to hurry so that I wouldn't be caught.

Although drawn to the excitement of the dark horse that stood prancing in place, I mounted the white horse quickly, and the black one followed.

Silently we turned left and headed into the heavy green forest. The massive gray castle was soon obscured.

I was riding bareback, and eventually threw back the hood. Later I threw off the entire dark blue cape, and rode naked. I seemed to become one with the white horse.

The trail wound up a mountain, but just before dusk, we headed down. The trail changed to a steep, walled canyon of orange-colored rock and dirt, desolate, but lovely, with no growing things in sight. As it narrowed, the horses stepped more steadily and slowly.

Nightfall passed almost unnoticed and at daybreak the narrow canyon opened on a desert with tiny wildflowers of all colors, thinly scattered across the flat landscape. Hazy mountains loomed far in the distance.

I got down from the white horse and watched in amazement as the white horse joined its black companion in kicking and frolicking.

The sight of the two horses set against the backdrop of the green-blue mountains, with the morning sun sending shafts of light through their tousled manes has remained a beautiful memory.

We walked then, maybe for days, until the earth became slightly hilly, with a few scattered trees and bushes about. We were coming to an area where other people had been, and I got on the white horse again to speed us along. We came to a corral, with gray-weathered boards, long deserted and needing repair. Once inside, I glanced about at the rolling hills, scattered with tiny flowers of every color.

Then a dark brown bull appeared from the east coming toward me from one of the hills. It seemed as startled as me. It had a pink flower trapped on its horn. Eventually I approached the bull and touched it in the center of the forehead.

As we stepped from the corral, a red stallion appeared. It stood beside a dilapidated gate and then raised high on its back legs and struck at the air threateningly.

The white horse glared at the powerful, red horse and told it to calm down. Then the white horse turned to the black one and said, "I don't care for that beast. It is arrogant."

The black horse was in awe of the red stallion, and whispered to me that the red horse would eventually be of use to us. It wanted to join us, but the white horse said, "no."

I thought the red horse was the most beautiful creature I had ever seen, and I sensed that the red horse knew it too. We left it stamping its hooves in the yellow-tinged dust.

At nightfall, we slowed down because we had entered a dark, dank, swampy area. The white horse stumbled frequently on dark green vines that covered the endless bog.

Each time it stumbled, the black one nudged it on as if to say, "You can make it."

I wanted to dismount so the white horse would have an easier time of it, but it told me to stay put. Then it began sinking into the swamp. I yelled to the black horse for help, and it began pushing on the rump of the white one. Still, it sank deeper until my legs were stuck in black mud.

Its white head nearly disappeared from sight and the black horse began pulling at me with its teeth. It ordered me to get out of the mud, and the white horse, disappearing fast, said it was weary. After it disappeared from view, the black horse said the white horse would be okay and would join us later.

As we were about to leave, the red horse emerged from the mud, and joined us on the journey. I rode the black one, though, but kept my eye on the red beauty.

Often, the red horse pranced and danced, kicked its back legs outward in a show of strength and shouted, "I am beautiful. I am strong." But the outbursts became fewer as we continued the journey, and it seemed to grow more serene. Its strength and beauty would always remain but only a touch of the haughtiness would stay.

On a grassy knoll, in the middle of the night, the black horse told me that I must continue on alone. I was frightened, and said so. I wanted to know where they were going, and the black horse said it would show me, but then I would have to leave.

Riding the black horse, we ascended skyward to a bright, flowing, starlit deck. We were met there by the white horse. Without a spoken word, the three horses grouped close together and left me standing alone. "Go now," they said. "We are one and you may not witness us any further."

With that, they were gone and I was left standing at the edge of a carpet of glowing yellow flowers. It wasn't journey's end, though, because I knew I was looking for a carpet of white flowers.

Other sequences followed her through the years, and she eventually called on the horses during meditation.

The color of the horses, and even the horses themselves, can have many different interpretations. In some old folk tales, a riderless horse was a symbol of death. In other interpretations, the horse can stand for freedom. Other interpretations exist—black and white for good and evil, and red for sexuality. Or the white horse could stand for enlightenment, and the red horse for energy.

Likewise, the many other colors in the dream convey different messages to the dreamer.

To decipher this dream by color, one might consider the following meanings attributed to them by some dream interpreters:

- **Green:** Knowledge, understanding, learning, peace.
- **Orange:** Increased awareness. An urge to hurry.
- **Brown:** Abundance and fullness. It can also mean confusion.
- **Multicolored:** Increased sense of security.
- **Red:** Rage, anxiety, or increased self-esteem.
- **White:** Awakening of spirituality. Higher self-learning.
- **Yellow:** Happiness, beginnings.
- **Black:** Acknowledging the dark or shadow side of yourself.
- **Pink:** Softness, flowing love, lack of fear.

CULTURAL ASSOCIATIONS

Although universal, or archetypal, dreams occur in all cultures, they take on different meanings within those societies. For example, in ancient societies such as Greece, a snake signified sickness; to the Assyrians, it meant protection from an angel; and to the Egyptian, it meant that an argument would be settled.

Thus, cultures may dream in the same symbols, and the same vivid colors may appear in the dream, but they have different meanings to different people.

A dream I once had about a room full of snakes has received various interpretations by different people, including some therapists. To one, the snakes stood for awakening sexuality; to another, because of its circular representation, it meant getting in touch with my feminine side.

Colors, too, take on a variety of meanings, depending on the context in which they are set. Green to one person may represent increased knowledge; to another it may portend an awakening to the beauty of nature and concern for the environment.

So each individual holds the key to unlocking the meaning of his or her dreams, including its colors. One method of interpreting your own dreams is to ask yourself upon awakening, "What did that dream mean to me?"

Newport, California, psychologist Bobbe Sommers, director of Speaker's Bureau Unlimited, said one way to remember dreams and get a handle on interpreting them is to give them a label immediately after awakening, like giving a title to a movie. Then ask yourself what emotions you felt, such as sadness, happiness, anger.

Ask yourself what you believe the dream meant. How did you feel about the colors in the dream? Did they have any special significance to your way of thinking?

Many dream experts believe this method, or similar self-interpretations, are more reliable than following the dictates of the variety of dream interpretations.

THE COLOR OF DREAMS

Hundreds of books have been written on the symbolic meaning of dreams, including their colors, and not all are in agreement.

Although each individual must ascertain what the dream and the colors meant to him or her, some of the folklore on the symbolic color meanings of dreams can be fun to use. A few are:

- **Dreaming in a mixture of bright colors:** Increased security and success.
- **Blue:** Liberation from worry. Help from others.
- **Black:** Upcoming difficulties.
- **Brown:** Luck with money.
- **Red (bright):** A warning to curb the temper.
- **Red (deep):** Favorable news.
- **Green:** Related to travel or news from another country.
- **Gray:** A period of waiting.
- **Lavender:** Temporary unhappiness or disappointments.
- **Orange:** Delay.
- **Pink:** Success.
- **Purple:** Future success in social affairs.
- **Yellow:** Setback or struggle.
- **White:** Success is promised.

MEDITATING IN COLOR

Meditation or visualization that includes color is widely used in some medical circles today, but it can be used by anyone wanting to enhance his or her life.

- Meditate in the cosmic red to feel energized.
- Try cosmic clear green to soothe jangled nerves.
- Feel the flu coming on? Try meditating in cosmic blue.
- Meditating in orange will produce a joyful, happy feeling.
- Yellow will enhance intellectual capabilities.
- Vibrant pinks establish the love connection.
- Translucent blue can calm a person.

Breathing techniques are at the core of meditating in color, just as color is in singing. "If the breath is in line, everything else will work," says Nicki Cohen, professor of music therapy and voice at Texas Woman's University. Humans generally quit breathing correctly with the tummy once they outgrow the infant crawling stage. They stand up and hold in the stomach, and begin a more shallow breathing in the upper torso.

"When we teach singing, we emphasize that the diaphragm pushes down when we take a breath. Not only does the diaphragm push down, but the ribs push out, so we get a lower expanded feeling like that taught in yoga," says Cohen.

The type of breathing that gets one into the lower realms of the body actually reduces stress, and gives one a feeling of contentment. When visualization of color is added, one can slip into a meditative state that adds to the relaxation.

To begin, position yourself comfortably to allow room for the stomach to expand, and let your body relax. Focus your attention on inhalation and exhalation. Continue this breath exercise until it is not forced, but seems to come naturally and comfortably.

Once that is achieved, close your eyes and imagine healthful and nourishing colors flowing in with your breath, and troubling colors flowing out as you exhale. These colors can be of your own choosing, or whatever happens to flow into your mind's eye.

CHAPTER 5

The Effects of Color and Light On Health

The changing panoply in light and dark of the twenty-four-hour day causes various physiological and psychological actions in the body and is responsible for the light waves people see as color. When someone has a "sunny" disposition, or a "black" or "dark" mood, more is at work than we suspect. Lightness and darkness, as well as the visible colors, affect the entire body, and its responses.

Instinctual response to color, such as the brightness of yellow, contrasted to the darkness of night, is linked to the more primitive midbrain, which regulates body temperature, libido, and hunger. It is also involved in pleasure, pain, and depression.

The more subtle distinctions of color are less reactive and instinctual, and more conditioned by the cerebral cortex, the outer portion of the brain, which is less primitive. It relies more on education and conditioning since it controls higher mental functions. Between these two portions of the brain, plus some instinctual behavior and the body's circadian rhythm, color and light sensitivity is born. Because color is linked to moods, it may also explain why a person might buy a blouse or shirt of a particular color one day, and the next day wonder why he or she ever bought the piece of clothing.

But color, which is light, or wavelengths from the sun, cuts far deeper than color moods. Scientific studies show that a lack of light may alter the interplay of a variety of brain chemicals creating conditions such as jet lag, problems with sleep, spring depression, and the winter blahs, called seasonal affective disorder when the winter blahs become chronic and debilitating.

SPRING DEPRESSION

Scientists are taking up the spring gauntlet and acknowledging what poets, philosophers, and lovers have suspected for ages—that the vernal equinox, which appears near the end of March and is commonly known as the beginning of spring, can be a time of disturbance for the human psyche. A mixed bag of sleep and energy fluctuations, feelings of euphoria or depression, and changes in eating patterns, as well as such urges as to "run away from it all," occur when daylight and dark become equal in length. This phenomenon is possibly brought about by a change in light that affects our glands and internal reaction, according to medical researchers.

One theory is that the increased intensity and longevity of sunlight in spring is measured by the brain as it filters through the eyes. The light information makes its way to the pineal gland at the base of the cerebrum, decreasing the production of melatonin, a hormone that helps keep mood and energy levels in check.

The late Helmut Landsberg, a meteorologist at the University of Maryland, was among the first to suspect that the rapid changes and transitions that occur in spring are connected to the rapid increase in light intensity that takes place between February and April. He also felt that rapid changes in temperature from low to high and low again, create stress on the body and mind.

Michael Gauquelin, a French psychologist and author of *How Cosmic and Atmospheric Energies Affect Your Health*, noted that although romance blooms in the spring and fresh plans are made, it also can be a period of flaring tempers triggered by rapid changes in mood. Fast-paced changes can increase impulsive behavior—both for good and ill.

Dr. Norman E. Rosenthal, director of seasonal studies at the National Institute of Mental Health in Bethesda, Maryland, says that new research shows that the human body is more attuned to the seasons than was previously believed. "It's a seasonal rhythm of the kind that you see in other animals," he says.

Rosenthal believes that the dramatic mood change contingent with the change from winter's dark to spring's light is linked to a type of hibernation. "It most definitely is a hibernating effect. Some do it with a bang and some with a whimper. You see it the same way in people year after year, and it makes you wonder if in our cave days we hibernated in winter. That's one explanation," says Rosenthal. He believes that those who enter spring with a bang are the same ones who during the winter oversleep, overeat, crave high-calorie foods, and gain weight—leftovers from times when hibernation may have been a matter of survival.

With renewed spring energy, not only may a person experience wanderlust, lethargy, and a host of other mood changes, but as Tennyson wrote in the seventeenth century, "In the Spring a young man's fancy lightly turns to thoughts of love." Indeed, conception is highest in April and May, according to the National Center for Health Statistics. There is no evidence, however, to support the notion that levels of testosterone increase in males during the spring months. Reasons for renewed sexual energy remain elusive.

"Spring is a special time for all ages. It's a time when people should fee free to express joy in living and in loving," says Ruth Weg, an authority on human sexuality at the University of Southern California.

Suicides also proliferate during the spring months. Many people still erroneously believe that the suicide rate rises during the Christmas holidays, when, in fact, it goes down during that period. The U.S. Centers for Disease Control found that between 1969 and 1978 suicides were seasonal—above average all spring and below average all winter. French sociologist Emile Durkheim noted more than fifty years ago that suicides increased in the spring.

Researchers offer a variety of reasons for this seasonal increase in suicide. The *British Journal of Psychiatry* reports that "the pre-summer peak in suicide reflects the hope among the unhappy and the lonely that the end of winter will bring an end to the social isolation and depression brought about by the cold weather. Spring comes but leaves matters unchanged. The post-summer did not bring about a change in life circumstances and the resultant feelings of hopelessness."

Other researchers have found that youths tend to commit suicide more during the spring, especially in March. It is speculated that children are particularly vulnerable, because spring presents itself as a period of hope and rebirth, which can be intolerable to a child in despair, according to Bem P. Allen, professor of psychology at Western Illinois University.

Additionally, research has shown that more than a third of serious mental disorders such as mania and cyclic depression follow seasonal patterns, and are in part linked to light. But great strides have been made to treat seasonal affective disorder (SAD), which manifests in the winter months as general sluggishness, decreased sexual drive, and feelings of hopelessness and worthlessness.

SEASONAL AFFECTIVE DISORDER

Mental health professionals are using bright lights and other agents that mimic summer conditions of light and color to treat those who suffer from seasonal affective disorder. The condition may seriously affect up to 12 million people, and mildly affect up to 26 million in the United States.

Some researchers believe that winter depression is a form of hibernation, because people who are affected tend to load up on carbohydrates, sleep longer than usual (up to fourteen hours a day), and report loss of energy. More people who live in states with heavy, persistent cloud cover, and in northern areas where people leave for work in the mornings when it's dark, and return in darkness suffer from SAD. Alaska's winter months are considered about the worst. A study in Washington, D.C., during the winter found that about 15 percent of the population there were mildly depressed, and 5 percent had major winter depressions. Other studies show that about 10 percent of New Hampshire's population experience depression during the winter, compared to about 1 percent in Florida, considered a sunshine state.

Many urban people are clustered in offices where they see no natural light, or ever get a peek at the sun shining when it does come out. The depression linked to SAD appears to be the result of lack of synchrony between body temperature and sleep cycles which are regulated by the body's clock that is regularly reset by morning light. Body temperatures rise and fall in a daily (circadian) rhythm that is regulated by this natural body clock, that is, in effect, rewound by sunlight.

Most people's lowest body temperature occurs about two to three hours before their normal time to awake. The body clocks of those with SAD, though, feel the effects of a natural tendency for the body to respond to a twenty-five-hour day, and that causes temperatures to reach their lowest levels just before awakening, says David Avery, associate professor of psychiatry at Harborview Medical Center in Seattle.

"Light is the main synchronizer of the biological clock," he says. The twenty-five-hour internal day that guides most life on the planet is the reason why most people find it easier to switch from the spring/summer daylight savings time to the fall/winter standard time when they gain an hour. The body is more in sync with this longer day.

Standard treatments for SAD involve the simulated use of bright lights, about five times greater than the lighting in an office, or between 2,000 to 2,500 lux (a unit of illumination). Current research is trying to determine how much illumination, and when. Thus far it seems that bright lights in the morning are the most effective, according to Avery.

Yet, it has been found that a few SAD patients who suffer from insomnia, and whose body clocks are set to an earlier awakening than normal, respond best to bright light treatment in the evening.

Additional studies indicate that gradually increasing the bright light in the morning to simulate a dawn effect may work best of all. Although not conclusive, "dawns" of varying duration and intensity appear to shift the body's temperature cycle counterclockwise.

Subjects in earlier studies had been awakened to receive the bright light treatments. Using dawn simulation, lighting is introduced while they are still asleep.

Avery says that the retina is especially sensitive to light in the early morning hours and that small amounts of light, especially from the red end of the visible spectrum, are transmitted through the eyelids. Additionally, dim light activates the rods that respond mostly to green light.

"So far, there is relatively little data saying that the spectrum of light makes that much difference," says Avery, "although it is suspected that a green wavelength might be better than a red one. Ultraviolet light, though, as once believed, isn't necessary for therapeutic use of light."

It's believed that light, of whatever brightness, intensity, or time applied, suppresses melatonin secretion, a hormone released by the pineal gland in the brain that causes drowsiness and interacts with a number of other bodily functions.

In addition to therapy, Avery says that people whose moods seem to be affected by gloomy weather often benefit from vacations in sunny locales or taking morning walks, even when the sky is overcast. People who suffer from SAD to any degree can also lighten up their homes by removing heavy draperies, painting walls light colors, adding skylights, adding brighter lighting, replacing dark wood furniture with light-toned pieces, and cutting back shrubbery that interferes with natural light.

LIGHT IN THE CLASSROOM

A few years ago, research by Dr. John Ott of Sarasota, Florida, found that full-spectrum lighting calmed down and lessened learning and reading disabilities in hyperactive school children.

Studies presented at the 1993 American Psychological Association meeting in Toronto, Canada, carried the concept further. Warren E. Hathaway, Ph.D., of Edmonton, Alberta, Canada, found that among three hundred school children, ages ten to twelve, that full-spectrum, UV-enhanced fluorescent lighting had better attendance records and greater achievement gains than students at schools with sodium-vapor lighting (common fluorescent lighting).

Additionally, the students with the UV-enhanced fluorescent lighting suffered from fewer dental cavities. Hathaway believes the studies add weight to other research showing that workers who spend most of the daylight hours indoors in facilities with unnatural light, should also receive the benefit of full-spectrum lighting.

Hathaway explains in a paper presented at the 1993 Annual Convention of the American Psychological Association that sunlight contains all colors in relatively uniform amounts, but that not all artificial light sources accurately reproduce the full spectrum of sunlight.

OTHER USES OF LIGHT THERAPY

Simulated light therapy at varying hours during the day has been found effective for treating jet lag, shift workers who suffer nighttime fatigue, and the elderly whose circadian rhythms alter with age, according to researchers Donald L. Bliwise, Ph.D., and Joseph D. Weissman, M.D., of Emory University School of Medicine.

Because the body's circadian rhythms are constantly interacting with its external environment, it is influenced by zeitgebers (time cue givers), noise, meals, illness, stress, and daylight and darkness. Problems in these areas results in sleep or alertness dysfunction.

Bliwise and Weissman's studies on night-shift workers indicate that about 20 percent of them fall asleep on the job. The body's natural rhythms dictate that nighttime is the time

L

to sleep. Deprivation causes mood swings, gastrointestinal problems, decrease in job performance, and general malaise, to say nothing of its psychological effects.

Unfortunately, lost sleep due to shift work cannot be made up on weekends, and the researchers say it's better to stay on the same sleep schedule required by the job in order to give some continuity to a readjusted sleep cycle.

Constant shift changes are also taxing on the body, and the researchers have found that shift changes from day to evening or evening to night, seem to have an easier time adjusting than those who change in reverse, such as evening to day.

They suggest that workers who must stay on a night shift should be exposed to extremely bright lighting on the job. Normal room brightness runs between 200 to 300 lux, and night workers should be exposed to between 2,000 to 3,000 lux.

Additionally, workers driving home in the morning should wear dark sunglasses to counter the effect of bright sunlight on the circadian rhythm. Workers should also delay sleep until the afternoon.

READJUSTING THE SLEEP CLOCK

Light from the sun is important to maintaining natural sleep habits which are dependent on our circadian rhythms. All living things function according to this rhythm.

Yet, it's not uncommon to hear people brag about how few hours sleep they require to get through the day, as if fewer hours spent sleeping means they are more vigorous and productive.

Sleep experts say these people are wrong. They delude themselves into thinking they're at full sail when they are really at half mast. If they need alarm clocks to rouse them in the morning, chances are it's due to sleep deprivation. A person will wake up to his or her own internal timing mechanism if he or she is getting enough sleep, and the best wake-up call in the morning is sunlight because it resets the biological clock.

"We know that before the advent of the electric light bulb people slept about an hour more. In Abraham Lincoln's time, the data available shows that most people got about eight and one-half hours of sleep instead of the seven and a half they get today," says Philip M. Becker, director of the Sleep/Wake Disorders Center at Presbyterian Hospital and professor of psychiatry at the University of Texas Southwestern Medical Center at Dallas. "A good source of light can allow people to stay up longer, and now that we have a global economy, we expect people to be up day or night to monitor people in other parts of the world. It breaks down the circadian rhythm," he says.

Also, "A lot of people get out of bed in a darkened room at seven o'clock in the morning, put on dark glasses when they get into their cars, and never get any real sunlight," says Dr. German Nino-Murcia, a sleep expert in Palo Alto, California.

She says that some new studies show that exposure to natural light or artificial light that mimics the sun's natural light can help reset a person's biological clock. Studies have shown for some time that wakefulness is controlled by a cluster of nerve cells in the brain that controls the release of certain hormones. But more recent studies have added that exposure to light on the retina of the eye is the most important factor in how the body determines what time of day it is.

Howard Roffwarg, M.D., a psychiatrist at the University of Texas Southwestern Medical Center in Dallas, says that one to two hours of this type of light treatment can reset the body's natural sleep rhythm.

Several sleep experts envision booths in airports where

foreign travelers can lessen the effects of jet lag with doses of this artificial sunshine.

The studies on sleep deprivation are important because a substantial number of Americans, perhaps the majority, are functionally handicapped by sleep deprivation on any given day, according to a report by the National Commission on Sleep Disorders Research. Indirect cost for the malaise, such as lowered productivity or automobile accidents, is estimated at $150 billion. Direct costs, for treatment of a number of ills related to sleep deprivation, is estimated at $15.9 billion.

Studies have shown that constant lighting in hospital nurseries disrupts the natural circadian rhythm of plasma human growth hormone, which requires a balance of natural dark and light cycles to function properly.

Other studies, just in their infancy, involve light therapy for Alzheimer's patients. Dr. Robert Green, at the Department of Neurology, Emory University, is studying the effects of how certain types of lighting affect the sleep of Alzheimer's patients who often have problems with sleep. The theory is that treatment with full-spectrum lighting may help induce sleep, since their brains process less of this natural light than normal because of brain cell degeneration.

LIGHT AND MENSTRUATION

Lack of light may create forms of natural hibernation and other innate human responses, long forgotten in the sometimes artificial setting in which men and women live today. Research also indicates that light helps determine female ovulation. Some scientists have postulated that extra artificial light could be used during certain days of the month to serve as a type of birth control.

It's believed that light stimulates the pineal gland after entering the eyes and traveling to the brain. The pineal gland is responsible for releasing or halting the flow of melatonin, a hormone associated with sleep inducement, and serotonin, a neurotransmitter involved with the nervous system, and with the release and regulation of other hormones.

Faber Birren writes in *Color and Human Response* that menstruation may cease in Eskimo women during the long Arctic nights, and that the libido of Eskimo men may also lie dormant. It serves as a natural form of birth control, with Eskimo children generally born nine months after the advent of spring and the long sunny days.

Birren quotes an article by Francis Woidich, "The Resonant Brain," that discusses a South American village where the birth rate dropped after electric lights were installed, the theory being that sexual activity is minimized in daylight.

Other related studies at the Sam and Rose Stein Institute for Research on Aging at the University of California, San Diego, indicate that ordinary bedside light can influence menstrual cycles. The research has centered on women with excessively long cycles, showing that when night lights of certain brightness are used, the cycle can be shortened.

DYSLEXIA

The term *dyslexia*, a Greek word, literally means word trouble, and may affect as many as a tenth of the nation's school-age population, according to Franklin R. Manis, assistant professor of psychology at the University of Southern California.

Dyslexia, however, is not the same as scotopic sensitivity syndrome (SSS), which is a dysfunctional response to specific wavelengths of light, and is associated with certain cells in the eye's retina. "It is a vision problem, and not true dyslexia," says Manis, adding that a few dyslexics may also have SSS in addition to the multiple problems associated with dyslexia.

"The vision can be corrected, but they will still have the problems associated with classic dyslexia," he says.

Some proponents of colored plastic overlays placed on reading material claim that dyslexics can be helped by their use, but most experts refute the notion. Manis, among others, says too few, wide-ranging studies have taken place to prove anything. Additionally, it's never been proven that dyslexics have a greater proportion of vision problems than the general population.

One of the criterion for dyslexia is when a person has the intellectual capacity to read, and the desire, but can't. "It's not a single disorder. Primarily it's a language problem associated with processing information. It's believed to be a brain malfunction, with some autopsy studies showing certain areas of the brain not developed," says Manis.

Proponents of the overlays, though, often lump SSS with dyslexia, cautioning that the treatment is not the same as Irlen lenses, widely used in Australia for SSS and dyslexia. The lenses were developed by educational psychologist Helen Irlen of the United States, whose book *Reading By the Colors* was released in 1991.

Proponents of the plastic overlays claim the overlays are more effective, and less costly than the lenses.

THE PROTECTIVE SUN

The effects of the sun can be both a deterrent to cancer, and a cause. Too much exposure, and skin cancers can form. Too little, and the body responds internally.

Colin Chignell, Ph.D., and colleagues at the National Institute of Environmental Health Sciences in Raleigh, North

Carolina, divided mice into three groups that belonged to a strain bred to develop tumors as they matured.

Each group was lit by a different color of fluorescent lamp—pink, cool-white, and daylight-stimulating.

After nearly one and a half years, the daylight-stimulating lamp mice had the greatest resistance to cancer. Those under the pink and cool-white lamps developed tumors after forty-two to forty-seven weeks, while the full-spectrum (daylight stimulating) ones didn't develop tumors until the fifty-first week.

Chignell suspected that a hormone, prolactin, secreted by the pituitary gland, may have had something to do with the outcome since light affects the pituitary gland. These mice also have retinal degeneration, and are blind by the time they are a few weeks old. The scientists believe it is possible that light affects these mice through the skin.

DAMAGING EFFECTS OF THE SUN

The sun, although it can be life-giving, can also be detrimental to a person's health. People are more aware than ever before of the damaging effects of sun, especially its link to skin cancer, and especially melanoma, the potentially deadly skin cancer. However, in 1993 the American Cancer Society announced some unexpected findings, along with those some have come to accept, related to skin cancer.

In a six-year study involving 1.2 million people, researchers found that the risk of melanoma is increased by use of diuretics, occupational exposure to x-rays or radioactive materials, a family history of skin cancer or colon cancer, personal history of skin cancer, higher socioeconomic status, a white-collar occupation, and advanced education.

Some of the findings seemed surprising, such as a higher socioeconomic status and white collar occupation, but the two may be linked to less short-term exposure to sun and more to high exposure on weekends because of their jobs and lifestyle.

Other studies, though, trace the accumulated effects of sun exposure to other causes.

Exposing young children to the sun increases their risk of developing malignant melanoma as adults, and may be more dangerous than continued exposure as an adult.

If children lived in sunny locales during their early years, the increased risk follows them no matter where they eventually reside, according to Thomas Mack, M.D., professor of preventive medicine at the University of Southern California School of Medicine. Even if precautions are taken as adults, their childhood exposure sets the stage for a condition that annually afflicts more than 28,000 people, a figure that increases yearly by 4 percent.

Those who spent childhoods in northern states enjoy relative safety from skin melanoma even though they may have spent decades as adults in sunny locales, says Mack, principal investigator of studies that tracked 4,611 cases of melanoma among white residents of Los Angeles County for ten years. Those born in sun belt areas, and who stayed as adults, retained a 60 percent increased risk of melanoma.

Those raised as children in sun-belt states, but who lived as adults in northern climates, continued to have a two and a half times greater risk of melanoma, says Mack.

Mack calls the condition a "time bomb" since emphasis has been placed on protection as an adult, and links to depletion of the ozone layer that shields the earth from harmful radiation. "Whatever is happening, is happening early," he says. "It could be that we get 80 percent of our sun exposure as children because we're outside more, or it could be a special susceptibility that sets the process in motion at that earlier age. We just don't know yet."

The development of most melanoma requires a long latency period, so the current increase in the deadly skin cancer isn't the result of ozone depletion, according to Mack. "The ozone is bad, but nothing we would see yet in terms of melanoma."

Current melanoma rates are the result of diagnoses in older people who followed the mid-century trend of sun exposure, and don't reflect recent effects of the sun, which could only be present in the younger generation, he says. "Decades must pass before it will be possible to assess the real impact of recent ozone depletion on melanoma risk."

In the meantime, don't throw out the sun screens and resume the practice of sunbathing. "Common sense should prevail. Don't get too much sun at any age," says Mack.

OTHER MEDICAL ASPECTS OF SUN EXPOSURE

Certain types of light from the spectrum are used to treat illness. Infrared radiation can be used for relief of certain aches and pains. Ultraviolet radiation helps prevent rickets, stimulates vitamin D formation, destroys bacteria, molds, and possibly some viruses. Exposure to the sun, or simulated full-spectrum lighting, can increase white cell activity, is important for the growth of children, and is essential to hormonal balance. Blood pressure is also affected by exposure to the sun.

Although jaundiced newborns are treated with blue light, some medical researchers believe that full-spectrum lighting such as that from the sun, contains the needed essential blue light, and is easier for nurses to use since they can more easily detect changes in an infant's skin color.

THE BRAIN:
COMING TO YOU NOW IN COLOR

The use of color is heightening people's understanding of the brain's function. No longer is the brain perceived as a "gray mass." Color mapping of the brain has become standard in many medical diagnosis, so people can now envision the brain in color. Positron emission tomography (PET) and magnetic resonance imaging (MRI) scanning allows researchers for the first time to investigate the mental processes of healthy individuals. Researchers can watch the brain to see which areas are involved in specific functions.

To do a traditional PET scan, researchers inject radioactive water into the patient's bloodstream. Hot blood finds its way to the brain and since active regions use more blood than inactive ones, they light up and that area is captured on special detectors, and translated into color.

Researchers have discovered that it takes less time for the brain to be stimulated in the hot spots when the same stimulation, such as a particular word, is used over and over. The brain has already coded for the stimulus, much the same way that a person learns to drive a car. Eventually, certain movements become easier because people react to them automatically.

Scientists at Washington University in St. Louis using PET in 1993 recorded images of the section of the brain that is activated when a person remembers a word.

At the same time, researchers at Massachusetts General Hospital used a special, new and faster type MRI to map portions of the visual cortex being stimulated by light. The new method employed no radiation.

Another device, similar to a PET, is the brain electrical activity mapping (BEAM) device which records the electrical activity of the brain and converts it into color maps that indicate the degree and distribution of the activity over the head. It is similar to a weather map showing the distribution of temperatures across the country.

It provides a computer color image of the functioning brain. The image is compared to a normal plate or database that allows instant comparisons to detect subtle abnormalities. It not only detects tumors, strokes, and hemorrhage, but can detect emotional and psychological disorders by assigning color codes, or maps of the brain's electrical activity.

From the rhythms of the body, to the mind itself, color and light strum the human form much like a musician playing the cords of a stringed instrument. He or she can produce notes of harmony, or those of discord. Color and light are there in illness and in health. It is a form of energy that surrounds and penetrates the body as surely as the probing fingers of a healer.

CHAPTER 6

Color Therapies

Metaphysical health practitioners use colors as energy treatments for spiritual and physical balance, and holistic psychotherapists use color to identify and treat psychological problems. Color therapy is also used in visualization exercises, and in meditation.

COLOR THERAPY AS COMPLIMENTARY MEDICINE

The use of color therapy is not as accepted in the United States, though, as it is in some European countries. Color therapists are reimbursed by the British government through its national health plan, as are many alternative health practices that are called "complimentary medicine." "A general practitioner has to approve or recommend the color therapy," says Howard Sun, who with his wife, Dorothy, operates the Living Color Institute in Hampstead, London.

They belong to two organizations for color therapists, the British Complimentary Medicine Association and the Institute for Complimentary Medicine.

Sun said during a phone interview that the wide acceptance of the practice in Britain has been brought about because of several television programs on the use of color therapy, public demand, and the Royal Family's use of homeopathic remedies.

Sun, author of *Color Your Life*, said his practice consists of a diagnosis, based first on a color analysis similar to, but different from, the Luscher Color Test (see Color Testing in this chapter). "It is something we developed as a psychological process that gives us a good insight into people, including their pathological and subconscious makeup." By determining these factors, plus taking a look at the individual's personality and health characteristics, it serves as a good tool to discover the person's total health status, according to Sun. Health status is linked to the colors the person chooses.

The difference between Sun's color test and Luscher's is that the former reflects an alignment with holistic philosophies. It works in conjunction with the basic chakra system. "People can learn to do it for themselves. We ask them to pick from colors and shapes laid out in front of them. We tell them how to choose and they choose, and then we reflect the findings back to them. It's an interactive process. We work together instead of just doing something to or for them," he says.

Sun's color test, "The Color Reflection Reading," incorporates only colors found in the rainbow—pink, red, orange, yellow, green, turquoise, blue, and purple. For analysis (which can be done by the individual), the colors are placed on particular shapes, such as circles, squares, triangles, pentagrams, and hexagrams. Sun believes colors are related to the right side of the brain and that shapes are perceived by the left side.

He is also influenced by Taoism. "It's in me. This is why I

use eight colors. Taoism is duality, and you can't have duality with an odd number."

Certain colors elicit various meanings, and the position in which a certain color is placed, and the shape of that selected colored piece leads to other levels of meaning and insight. "Colors directly affect the body. It's a young innocence therapy. We have found that it accelerates and brings things to the surface. It also helps to stimulate and work on the nervous system," says Sun.

"We see the personality type we are facing in relation to the colors they choose. There are subtle interrelationships that give us clues—the person's energetic makeup. We confirm this with them.

"What we have found since we developed it is that it increases people's intuition. They can take part in their self-growth, and it's fun to work with."

Sun calls the techniques used, "Dowsing," designed to pick up imbalances at the metaphysical level. He considers it a diagnostic tool. "The beauty about the color is that it lends itself to the person. A lot of fluidity in there."

Once the person's color balance is ascertained, color light treatment is given through colors radiating from a crystal. Light changes the clear crystal into a sort of prism that produces various forms of light energies. Then the therapist douses the body with his or her fingers, in conjunction with the energy of the light.

Sun believes the practice indicates where physical and mental blocks exist. As these blocks dissipate they produce new patterns that show any progress, which is carefully monitored.

Major differences from the Luscher Color Test, are the colors. Sun uses red, orange, yellow, green, turquoise, blue, violet, and magenta, as opposed to red-orange, green, dark blue, violet, yellow, brown, gray, and black. Both, though, use eight colors. "Some of the reasons for the colors are philosophical. We found that these two new colors, magenta and turquoise, are relevant to the New Age and the metaphysical movement because of the energy of the planets. We need these energies for balance. Magenta is all about humanity and passion. Turquoise is about change and consumption. Turquoise represents turning points in the environment. We need these energies if we are going to survive. These colors carry these particular energies."

Sun believes the depletion or the excessive use of some colors is damaging. "Outer space has more to do with yellow, and we've gone overboard with that. We have to turn back or we'll fall off the precipice. People are exploding in terms of disease and wars. Yellow makes us avoid contact from the other side—the more human side of us. We learn things on the yellow level—how to acquire skills to get a job. But socially and spiritually, few models exist."

Packman is very yellow, Sun notes.

Sun, of Chinese origin, is originally from Jamaica. Dorothy, his wife, was raised in Cypress. Originally he set out to become a Taoist priest. "And so I went out to look for a way to have a career. It just happens to be color therapy, but it is the principles of life, as opposed to life. It's about who we are. The energy is of awareness and transformation. Color transforms consciousness. Color raises awareness and so it is important that people recognize this. That's why we now have complimentary medicine. The way we have gone before doesn't work.

"I saw people doing things by rote. All these things happening inside. So I was a seeker in Jamaica, then New York, then Los Angles, then England. I'm affiliated with a group in Cypress—Magi's, who are considered wise people in Cypress."

COLOR TESTING

For a similar in-depth analysis on mood and temperament, or a psychological perspective, the Luscher Color Test, one of best-known tests created in the 1960s by

Dr. Max Luscher, a Swiss psychologist, reveals a person's psychological makeup according to his or her ordered selection of eight main colors. It is outlined in *The Luscher Color Test* book. Although the original work included 73 colors and was originally developed for use by psychiatrists, psychologists, and physicians, the shorter version is available in many libraries and is widely used by the layperson.

The selected preferences in color, based on spontaneous selection rather than on what looks best on the person, plus the order in which they are chosen, gives clues to the person's personality and mood.

The basic meanings of Sun's and Luscher's colors bear many likeness when the colors are the same or similar.

SUN	LUSCHER
Red: Intense, energetic, animated.	**Red/Orange:** Intense, energetic, passionate.
Blue: Gentle, passive, spiritual.	**Dark Blue:** Content, trustworthy, tranquil.
Purple: Spiritual, dignified.	**Violet:** Charming, needful, reliant upon others.
Yellow: Logical, well-spoken, intellectual.	**Yellow:** Hopeful, energetic, covets respect.
Green: Balanced, sincere, conscientious.	**Green:** Firm, steady, dislikes change.
Turquoise: Calm, spiritual, insightful.	**Brown:** Insecure, uncomfortable feelings.
Pink: Warm, friendly, compassionate.	**Gray:** A loner, uncommitted, self-stimulated.
Orange: Happy, courageous, cheerful.	**Black:** Dissatisfied, stubborn.

OTHER TYPES OF COLOR THERAPY

Color therapy can encompass color breathing in conjunction with visualization, or visualizing the chakra centers spinning in color throughout and surrounding the body.

A friend who has multiple sclerosis practices a type of color therapy while doing yoga. Yoga has been found to help control some bodily aspects of the debilitating disease. The friend practices yoga and color breathing in conjunction with standard medical practices to help keep the disease under control.

To relax at the beginning of her yoga sessions, she breathes in the healing colors of pink and yellow, and breathes out the colors brown and red. This is her own choice of colors, and works for her. She says it took her some time to actually "see" colors on her eyelids, which is much more difficult than simply seeing a space of color in the mind. Initially she could "think" the colors, but turning the vision into color on her closed eyelids took time and practice and was more difficult than the breath exercises.

Color therapy is used to stimulate or relax the body, and is sometimes achieved by shining certain colors into the eye. Blues have been found to ease some types of headaches. Red may help with some cases of dizziness since it increases blood pressure and pulse rates. Yellow light has been used to treat some mental disorders. Digestive problems have been treated with yellow, green or blue light.

In most situations, though, green can be used for nearly any type of healing. It is considered a balancing vibration of color.

Some medical scientists, though, consider color therapy simply a prop, even though they believe it is a good one. "In a lot of therapeutic conditions, you need a point of contact, like music or art. Color therapy provides that," says Stanley Coren,

Canadian psychologist, and specialist in the senses. "Anything that can focus a person's attention away from his or her problems, and that builds confidence is usable," he says.

Psychology, more than any other branch of medicine, realizes that medical treatment involves the whole person, and that includes the mind itself, and the feeling that the patient is taking some part in his or her own treatment. Color therapy may not reach in and manipulate the part of the body undergoing treatment, but it compliments medical intervention by making the treatment whole body, or holistic.

No ethical color practitioner would try to treat a broken arm or cancer with color therapy, but using it in conjunction with standard treatments might, in some cases, be beneficial.

COLORED OIL THERAPY

Aileen Penn, an aromatherapist in England, also uses colored oils for treatments. The more than eighty colored oils in crystalline bottles that she uses represent the chakras, personal choices associated with the aura of the individual, moods, and the life pattern of the person. In all cases, the oils are used for balancing the mental, spiritual, and physical world of the individual, according to Penn.

The oil therapy she uses is based on the aura-soma balance developed by the late Vicky Wall of England, a healer and spiritualist, and author of *The Miracle of Colour Healing*.

The oils, made from plant essences and extracts, can be used in their bottles for meditation, and as dowsing agents in association with certain parts of the body linked to the chakra system. Selection of certain colors by an individual can also indicate his or her life's purpose, evolution, soul purpose, and the energies of the future associated with that individual.

Shaking the bottles can also relate the type of energy an individual is dealing with at the time. Good energy is indicated when a bottle is shaken vigorously to form small bubbles that last for six seconds before the oil and water in the bottle separate. A cloudy formation indicates imbalance. Large bubbles indicate unrest and turmoil.

Practitioners might have a person select four bottles of different colored oils and then give readings from them on three levels—the spirit level, mental and emotional level, and the physical level.

For healing the body, a therapist might shake a specific colored bottle of oil, and then pass the bottle over a client's body where an aura is present. Once a determination is made on what particular organ or body part is in need of balancing, the healer will sometimes shake the bottle to mix the colored liquid, and rub it on the affected area.

The colors used, if the choice is to associate them with the chakra system, are similar to the traditional colors linked to them (see chapter 2), with minor exceptions. In colored oil therapy, pink is added for the reproduction area; the traditional green of the fifth chakra can be a blue/green; and magenta (purplish red), replaces the traditional violet or white associated with the center of the crown, or the higher self.

The use of oils is an outgrowth of ancient practices, including alchemy, whereby certain oils were believed to contain elements of the sun's spectrum. Symbolically, the oils then contained chi, prana, elan, vital, or universal, or ethereal energy.

THE PSYCHOLOGY OF COLOR

As well as the innate or learned psychological associations of color, people surround themselves with particular colors to establish body boundaries, or to enhance self-esteem, self-confidence, and a sense of security.

Defining boundaries by bright colors, or with tattoos firms up the sense of security, according to Seymour Fisher, professor of psychiatry at State University of New York, Syracuse.

"If you feel you are too open to intrusion or that your body is too fragile, wearing bright colors may be a way of protecting yourself," says Seymour. "Paranoid, schizophrenic women often try to protect themselves by wearing bright clothing to articulate boundaries. Tattoos can be another form of boundary protection. The dress and hair of punk rockers may do the same thing."

Seymour, author of *Body Experience in Fantasy and Behavior*, says it isn't just bright colors that establish these boundaries. Anything that is unusual, such as Madonna and her black clothing, sets up certain boundaries. If you look in the mirror and see yourself wearing something unusual, it highlights the sense of your body. It seems to make it more firm, strong, or substantial."

In addition to a sense of identity, perhaps with a particular gang, tattoos, in some cases, also enhance these boundaries, and serve as a substitute for self-esteem or security. "It's like wearing a uniform. It offers a sense of security and an identity with a particular group," says Seymour.

The group doesn't have to be a gang. Police officers gain a sense of security and identity with a uniform. So do nuns, although some studies have shown that certain nuns who changed from the old-style black habit to the newer, more modern, and freer clothing, gained a sense of security, and increased self-esteem.

By the same token, people can enhance security by the way their homes are decorated.

The following is a compilation of some of the various psychological meanings attributed to colors. Liking certain colors can be both positive and negative, depending upon one's personal perspective.

Beige
- Well-adjusted
- Can see both sides of a situation
- Mediocre

Black
- Negative
- Dramatic
- The unknown
- Dignified and sophisticated
- Death
- Mystifying
- Secure

Blue (Dark)
- Confident
- Conservative
- Responsive
- Reliable
- Tranquil
- Introspective
- Demanding

Blue (Light or Pale)
- Peaceful
- Loving
- Affectionate
- Idealistic
- Communicative
- Sincere

Blue Green
- Sophisticated
- Discriminate

- Egocentric
- Fussy
- Orderly

Brown

- Passive
- Receptive
- Homespun
- Reliable
- Has a sense of duty
- Has a subtle sense of humor
- Loyal

Gray

- Tranquil
- Peaceful
- Content
- Same
- Aloof

Green

- Tense
- Balanced
- Generous
- Loyal
- Sensitive
- Enduring
- Tenacious
- Persistant
- Self-esteem

Lavender

- Refined
- Gentle

- Romantic
- Creative

Orange
- Warm
- Creative
- Joyful
- Immediate
- Assertive
- Expressive

Purple
- Unconventional
- Spiritual
- Sensitive
- Moody

Pink
- Youth-oriented
- Loving
- Relaxed

Red
- Filled with energy
- Sexual
- Successful
- Impulsive
- Restless
- Extroverted
- Impatient

Taupe
- Neutral
- Fair

- Stable
- Easy

Violet

- Sensitive
- Intimate
- Mystical
- Unifying
- Enchanting

White

- Neat
- Orderly
- Critical
- Self-sufficient
- Cautious
- Motivated
- Spiritual

Yellow

- Cheerful
- Enthusiastic
- Intelligent
- Original
- Wise
- Optimistic
- Competitive
- Egotistical
- Variable

Yellow-Green

- Perceptive
- Isolationist
- Non-judgmental

COLOR AND EMOTIONS

People's moods and temperament dictate likes and dislikes in color, but can be transitory. Although people may have basic preferences in colors, some will appeal to them one day, and change the next, depending on their moods.

Selections from the following list should not be based on what colors look best on a person, what color a mate prefers, or what is trendy. Choice simply establishes a mood at the time of selection.

The choices can be made by selecting from colored crayons or pencils spread out in front of you. I've used this method many times during classes based on my book, *When Women Choose to Be Single*, that I conduct for community services at several community colleges.

They evolved from two drawings done by the women in attendance—one on how they perceive themselves as single, and how they see themselves with a mate. The book and the classes are designed to raise the self-esteem of single women, who, because of societal pressures, feel they aren't complete without a man. It's to show them they can lead rich, full lives as single women without a constant search to find a man. Originally, we discuss the drawings, themselves. Then I begin taking note of the choice in colors they select from the colored pencils I supply. We then discuss color, using the standard, accepted designations, as well as how they personally feel about the colors they have selected. Their choice of colors seem to be much in keeping with standard characteristics associated with colors.

They are:

- **Black:** Dissatisfaction with life at present, and one doesn't want anything or anyone to interfere with one's present state of mind. Many of the women acknowledged they were still angry about a previous breakup with a mate.
- **Blue:** A need to establish calm relationships with others, and develop trust and emotional peace with oneself. They were aware this was what they were striving for.
- **Brown:** Feelings of distress and a need for release from situations that makes some people feel uncomfortable and insecure. Some who used brown said they were considering counseling.
- **Gray:** Wanted to feel uncommitted, uninvolved, and to go inside themselves for stimulation. Gray produced light strokes on the paper, as if they wanted to remain anonymous.
- **Green:** A need to impress others with their opinions, and to have their say. They said they felt strong, but weren't ready to make any major changes in their lives.
- **Red:** Intense, animated, and feeling sexually liberated. Some who had never liked the color red, now said they wanted to live life to the fullest.
- **Purple:** Feeling charming and sentimental, with an urge to be taken care of. They wanted to flee from life's problems, and not take on so much personal responsibility.
- **Yellow:** It projected a hopeful outlook on life at the present time, with a need to engender respect from others. They wanted assurance that life was going to continue to be sunny.

Color therapy as it is used today is not a twentieth century phenomenon. Humans have been incorporating particular colors into their lives for centuries without rationalizing their use. People seem to know instinctively that they use certain colors depending on their moods and emotions. One woman said, "You know, I must have been in a funk. I surrounded myself with grays and browns. I eventually had to throw out a bunch of stuff and lighten up my world with some brighter colors." Or a person will say she needs to wear something bright on a particular day to help chase away the blues. Or take the case of the woman who said that once she turned fifty, she switched to pink lighting in the bathroom to give her a rosy, younger look when she put on her makeup. All are using color therapy.

CHAPTER 7

Symbolism and Mythology in Color

Although the origins of many color associations are not known, they have been passed down through the ages and offer a pallet of symbolism that is still widely used today. Sometimes they vary from culture to culture, and frequently likenesses exist. People continue to this day to establish their own mythologies and symbols pertaining to color (see sections in this chapter on color clichés and titles).

For example, not all Sun cards in the variety of available tarot decks are marked with exactly the same symbolism. Sally Nichols in *Jung and the Tarot: An Archetypal Journey* says the Sun card of the Major Arcana in the Marseilles tarot is marked by multicolored droplets falling from heaven around the sun, symbolizing a new stage of enlightenment and nourishment. Yet, other decks don't show the droplets on the Sun card, although multicolors in vision and dreams can mean increased learning and knowledge.

SPIRITUALITY AND COLOR

The world's religions have a long history of likenesses when it comes to color. In the Christian tradition:

- White is considered divine as it is in many religions, but not all.
- Wisdom has been considered gray.
- Victory is green.
- Glory is orange.
- Strength is red.
- Mercy is blue.

In color symbolism, the Heavenly Trinity is blue for God, yellow for the Son, and red for the Holy Ghost. Heaven is blue, earth, yellow, and hell is red. Green is Mother Nature. Red also symbolizes martyrdom and the blood of Christ. Gold and yellow are power, glory, and splendor, and regarded as the color of the soul.

Additionally, blue stands for hope, peace, and serenity. The Virgin Mary is often depicted in blue.

Purple takes on suffering. Many orders of nuns traditionally wore purple. Purple is also associated with royalty or wealth, such as, "Clothed in purple and fine linen."

White represents chastity, purity, and simplicity. It represents heavenly bliss and is associated with Easter and the Resurrection in the Christian tradition.

EASTERN TRADITIONS

White, though, rather than black, is the color of mourning for many cultures, including Hinduism.

Red, in some Eastern traditions, is the color of the

Kundalini, or life force of the base chakra. Kundalini is psychic energy that can arouse the spiritual, higher self, or divine energy.

The Kundalini is depicted by an archetypal serpent goddess, sometimes entwined around a staff, representing the staff of life, as in the Caduceus medical symbol. Kundalini is a Sanskrit word meaning a twisting gas or force. Tradition holds that when the essence of this gas or force travels upwards from the base of the spinal canal and enters the brain, it enhances spiritual illumination.

Gopi Krishna's writings translated in *Kundalini for the New Age* say that sound and light and vibrant colors are ever present in abundance since he tapped into the Kundalini.

GIFTS OF SPIRITUAL AWARENESS

Although not associated with organized religion, some mystics associate certain colors with the four different types of spiritual awareness or gifts. A individual will usually be strongest in one area.

- Prophetic people tend to wear shades of violet.
- Visionaries prefer yellow and orange.
- Intuitive people often wear red.
- Feeling people select blues.

Additionally, those with psychic ability are frequently associated with the color orange. When I worked as a reporter and wrote several stories about psychics, particularly one who had helped law enforcement officials on some of their cases, I often noted touches of orange in the decorating schemes of their homes. When I commented about this orange color in their homes, they seemed aware of its presence, and said they had always liked the color, and made certain it was used someplace for decoration. They didn't overuse it, because it was a stimulating color, but they, at least, had to have a touch of it.

Saffron, an old-world plant, with orange/yellow stigmas, has been used for centuries in the Mideast, for flavoring and coloring foods and medicines.

Violet colored auras are associated with spirituality and transformation, and is also one of the colors sometimes connected to the seventh chakra in the crown area symbolizing insight and enlightenment.

Red is considered an energetic color, and conjures up the feeling of immediacy and spontaneity which characterizes an intuitive person. And blue is introspective, idealistic, and tranquil, all attributes of feeling people who search within themselves for answers.

ANCIENT AND PRIMITIVE TRADITIONS

Many of the modern associations with color are based on ancient traditions.

White in ancient traditions was often associated with the gods who dwelt on white, snow-topped mountains. White was sacred to Zeus, king of the ancient Greek pantheon of gods. White animals were sacrificed to him by white-robed priests. White horses drew his chariot.

Yellow to the Navajo of North America, symbolizes the yei or Holy People. A single yei or Talking God, is related to the sunbeam, yellow clouds, yellow corn, and the yellow warbler.

Green connects people to the environment. The term, "It's green," today stands for being environmentally correct. The ancients, too, associated green with fertility, growth, and rejuvenation.

Black stands for death and regeneration in many cultures. Historically black has symbolized sin, sorrow, evil, and death in European cultures where they are steeped in black traditions with such representations as black widow's weeds, black armbands, a black hearse. "If somebody dies we put on black, and if we find ourselves surrounded by individuals all dressed in black, it makes us feel somber, or even depressed," says Stanley Coren, psychology professor at the University of British Columbia.

"In India, though, white is the color of mourning. So whether black or white, it is a learned cultural response that produces the same effects."

Because it is a cultural response, those from European backgrounds tend to believe that black for mourning is universal. "It is a typical problem. A culture finds something that works—that elicits a certain response—and we try to postulate some kind of science to justify the fact that it seems appropriate," says Coren.

It is one of the traditional colors of mourning. It was associated with secular asceticism in ancient times, and many religious or secular orders today wear it as a sign of denying a sensual life.

It is linked to the supernatural because of its powers of darkness. The Furies, the three avenging goddesses of Greek traditions, dressed in black. So do witches, warlocks, and practitioners of the blacks arts and magic.

Black is associated with death and destruction—"As black as hell." Count Dracula is menacing in black, and undertakers are associated with black.

Red is the color of blood and takes on many significant meanings, but one of its strongest is its link to women's menstrual flow.

M. Ester Harding writes in *Woman's Mysteries* that among primitive people women in menses were themselves taboo.

In various parts of the world women were considered "unclean" during this monthly cycle. During this time she had to observe many restrictions, such as staying away from the village, not touching certain objects, or was prohibited from walking in particular places. Some groups considered her untouchable at this time, and in some cases men were not even allowed to look upon her, lest they lose their power.

As well as viewing her as unclean, though, many primitive traditions also considered her very powerful during her menses—too powerful to take her usual place in tribal life.

Red then, is considered both powerful and a taboo. For instance, a red cross is a sign of taboo in many parts of the world. Red signifies danger. It is a very powerful color, both because it elicits certain physiological responses, and because of its psychological meanings.

Gray is mysterious. It conjures up smoke, fog, dissolution, ambiguity, the ethereal.

ANCIENT COLOR ASSOCIATIONS

Although the countries and cultures of the ancient world were more isolated from one another than they are today, certain associations with color were manifest and similar in many of those cultures.

Colors associated with the four ancient Greek elements:

- **Earth:** black
- **Air:** white
- **Fire:** red
- **Water:** white

The Chinese, though, recognize five elements:

- **Earth:** yellow
- **Fire:** red
- **Water:** black
- **Wood:** green
- **Metal:** white

The Jewish historian Josephus (first century A.D.) wrote of color associations.

- **Earth:** white
- **Air:** yellow
- **Fire:** red
- **Water:** purple

The fifteenth century artist Leonardo da Vinci laid down his own principles of colors.

- **Earth:** yellow
- **Air:** blue
- **Fire:** red
- **Water:** green
- **Darkness:** black

MYTHOLOGY AND COLOR

Certain colors are associated with ancient Greek, Roman, and Celtic mythological figures who were seen as powers of authority. In today's world, people also attribute colors to new figures of power, usually associated with esteemed fields of endeavor, or scholarly pursuits. One might think culture has substituted one group of gods and goddesses for another.

- **Saturn:** black
- **Jupiter:** orange
- **Mars:** red
- **Sun (Apollo):** yellow
- **Moon (Venus):** white
- **Venus or Mercury:** green or blue

- **Philosophy:** blue
- **Arts and letters:** white
- **Medicine:** green
- **Law:** purple
- **Science:** yellow gold
- **Engineering:** orange
- **Music:** pink

CREATING SYMBOLISM

As an example of how people endow colors with special significance in everyday life, and create their own symbolism with color, I once wrote a column called "What's a Conservative Color?" It nearly cost me my job since the newspaper I worked for was quite conservative. It was off the top of my head and went like this:

What color is a conservative?
I mean, liberals have been labeled pinko or, even worse—red—so conservatives certainly need a color.
They often try to wrap themselves in red, white, and blue, but since red is already taken (by liberals), that only leaves white

and blue.

That's too bad. Red is an energy color. Scratch red.

Picture the two remaining colors of white and blue waving in the breeze. That doesn't wrap so well around conservatives.

Blue, after all, is a sort of meditative color used by artists to tune into higher cosmic spirituality.

The conservatives I know aren't into meditation or cosmic anything.

Scratch blue.

Color me white wouldn't win any popularity contests in our diversified culture. White is best left to brides whose parents are so thankful she's finally getting married that they'll pay anything for the gown and dismiss the fact that she's been living with her boyfriend for four years.

Scratch white.

Perhaps conservatives can hire a color consultant—one of those people who basically use the color keys from a paint company to mix and match colors, shades and tints.

Color consultants can determine if you're a spring, summer, autumn or winter person.

I've been told I'm an autumn person—best in colors of falling leaves—and should wear certain shades of brown, gold, orange and green.

I don't see conservatives in autumn colors. They don't like to fall to the ground like leaves.

Scratch autumn colors.

Blue is a good color. However, we've already scratched it for other reasons. It is universally liked by most men, but some men prefer the near-blue colors of purple or lavender.

Spiritually color-conscious people say that women who wear purple or lavender aren't very domineering. They don't mind so much being bossed around by a man.

Scratch purple or lavender. Conservatives wouldn't like being bossed around by anyone.

With lavender we're getting closer to the shades of pink. Pink has been found to be a good color. It quiets people. Researchers tell us that if you leave a prisoner in a pink room, it will calm his or her nerves.

Oh, darn. Pink is already taken.

I like the color yellow. It has a lot of energy. If a person meditates in yellow, it's supposed to enhance his or her intellectual capabilities, according to some New Age philosophers.

That might not be a bad color for conservatives.

On the other hand, yellow has always been the color of "the coward."

"You yellow coward!"

Scratch it.

We've already scratched red because it's been given to liberals, which is too bad since it's such an energizing color. Just ask a bull.

I don't know too much about green, except it's a calming color. Trees and grass and lots of nice things are green. Emeralds are green. Mold is green too, but even it can be useful, as in the case of making penicillin.

Green, however, is the color of leprechauns. I also associate it with Robin Hood who robbed from the rich and gave to the poor.

Scratch green for conservatives.

How about brown? Brown is a nice safe color. It is considered the color of abundance.

I have always like the color brown, despite a remark by Tony Curtis several years ago that only boring people wear brown.

Brown has a nice sound to it. Conservatives can be called "brownies."

That may make the Girl Scouts angry. Their younger charges are called Brownies.

Oh, well, scratch brown.

What about dual colors? Black and white might make a

good combination.

Black and white color combinations are popular dress colors when the country is going through change, according to researchers who also chronicle the change in dress lengths and other colors in relation to the mood of the country (white and pastels are popular when the country is in harmony).

Black and white it is, then.

We could combine it and get gray, but that is an area that liberals travel in.

We'll just leave it black and white. It's nice to be associated with a color.

━━━━━━━━

People create their symbolisms in color, whether it be through a newspaper article or a written agreement for services, such as "I want it in black and white." People simply cannot escape the effects that color has on human life—not just in seeing colors, but in thinking about them, and transposing them to the world at large.

DIRECTIONS IN COLOR

Native Americans honor the four directions (although there are frequently six directions in ceremony because up and down are used). The four earthly directions, though, are sometimes associated with colors of races.

- **North:** white
- **South:** black
- **East:** yellow
- **West:** red

Native Americans incorporated color into most aspects of their lives, and are given or receive specific colors through visions, ceremony, and from family members or Holy Men.

The Tibetans, too, gave directions color, and associated the directions to the shapes of faces.

- **North:** yellow (square faced)
- **South:** blue (oval faced)
- **East:** white (crescent-shaped faced)
- **West:** red (round faced)

The ancient Irish also had directional colors:

- **North:** black
- **South:** white
- **East:** purple
- **West:** dun or dusky

TATTOOING OR BODY PAINT

Most societies use some form of body painting, whether it be traditional makeup, tattooing, or full body paint. Such body paint can signify social status, membership in a particular group or organization, age and marital status, war or peace, economic status, and a host of other variables. Painting a neighbor or friend can also be an act of reciprocity, and communion. Modern Australian bushmen spend hours decorating their bodies and those of others with patterns made of colored clay. The patterns may be symbolic, but the act is one of community.

Anthropology and sociology professor Eric Silverman of DePauw University, in Greencastle, Indiana, says the human body is a symbol for conveying messages about power, morality, values, ideals, and culture in the organization of societies everywhere.

"One way to think of it is that the body is a canvas and people are painting messages about who they are and how they wish their group to be portrayed and perceived by other people," he says.

Painted or tattooed body messages aren't as common in European countries and the United States, as they are in some cultures, such as the Motu on the islands off New Guinea, but Europeans and Americans send those same types of messages with their clothing. "Some people say they don't give any thought to clothing, and just put on anything. But that is a message still. It is a message of opposition," he says.

Body decoration, via cosmetics, is also a form of body decoration and sends many messages similar to those given with clothing. Tattooing, though, is on the increase in many cultures that don't have a long and varied history with it. "Tattoos on males for a long time were a symbol of rebellion. Now they're more a symbol of belonging to a particular group, whether that be the Hell's Angels or the U.S. Marines. The thinking is, 'Sure, I'm in the military now, but I want a permanent association with this group so that in forty years, it will still be a permanent association.' "

"It connotes a sense of permanence," says Silverman, and he hypothesizes that the sense of permanence is a major factor in the growing use of tattoos in both men and women.

"It's a possibility that tattooing in a society like America that is undergoing flux and constant change, stands as a symbol of permanence that might be comforting," says Silverman.

If a person can associate him- or herself with a particular group, whether it be religious, sports, anti-establishment, or even a prison group, it fosters this sense of permanence and a feeling of belonging.

Still, body paint and tattooing in industrialized cultures does not carry the same message that it does in tribal societies who consider it a vital link with tradition, culture, and community.

People in industrialized societies often use it to make a statement saying they are outside the mainstream. "If you think of a society as having a center of people who conform the most, as you move out toward the fringes, you find people purposefully tend to treat their bodies in opposite ways from the people at the center," says Silverman.

At the same time, it can be an act of rebellion. "There is a sort of sense where some people look at tattoos as being living art on the body. It's not in the museum to be looked at and then left. They are making a class statement and saying, 'You connoisseurs are snobs and don't know what's going on with my group, and people like me,'" says Silverman.

Tattoos can also serve as a rite of passage that lends a tangible concreteness to a significant life event, such as graduating from high school or college, an engagement, or even turning fifty.

Another reason for the popularity of tattoos, especially in the past ten years, is America's fixation on the body, which may be linked to the perception that the United States is in decline. Silverman believes that as the belief that the body politic is declining, the body beautiful becomes more important. "Symbolically, we are making the body stronger with an emphasis on physical fitness, and displaying the body."

Whatever the reason for a tattoo, Americans are establishing traditions as they proceed. Male tattoos tend to be visible and women's are only to be seen by someone who is intimate with them, according to Silverman.

Although tattooing and body paint is on an increase in some European countries and the United States, and a type of symbolism is being established, it is not as deeply imbedded in cultural traditions as it is in other societies, particularly those with a fixed hierarchy. Nor do the colors used take on the significance of those other societies.

For example, the Motu, studied by Silverman, commemorate their Hiri Voyages in massive outrigger canoes by tattooing the women of the village, who consider it a source of pride.

In some of the islands off New Guinea both sexes receive facial tattoos in colorful geometric designs. Only women, though, receive pigmented tattoos on their torsos to signify important life events. Some of the societies use excessively bright colors for women to signify wealth, sexuality, fertility, freshness, and health. Dark colors, painted on men, signify power and aggression.

Red, black, and white appear to be universal colors signifying, in order, blood and menstruation; semen and tribal continuity; and power and aggression.

Whatever the reasons for tattooing, it sends a complex message. "One way to think of it is that the body is a canvas and people are painting messages about who they are and how they wish their group to be portrayed and perceived by other people," says Silverman.

COLORS OF MAN AND WOMAN

In nearly all cultures, the top color choice is blue or red, with men preferring reds tinged with yellow, as in tomato, and women preferring their reds with a little blue, like Bing cherries. Brown is one of the least favorite of both sexes.

Certain colors, though, have traditionally been ascribed to men and women. Native Americans considered red, yellow, and black as masculine colors, while white, blue, and green were feminine.

When one looks toward the yin and yang of Eastern philosophy, or the West's archetypal psychology, an association of colors for men and women also exists.

C. G. Jung coined the terms "anima" and "animus," to represent the opposites of the male and female characters.

The two terms are a deeper approach to the Eastern philosophy of yin, the receptive female characteristics, and yang, the male power. Yin and yang are symbolic of all patterns in nature's processes.

The anima is likened to the yin, or feminine side, and the animus to the yang, or masculine, with the hidden feminine side of man as anima, and the hidden masculine side in women termed animus.

Between the two, it is seen that all living creatures and things of nature have attributes of yin or yang, or anima/animus.

In Taoism, harmony with nature is achieved through interaction of yin and yang. Nature itself is harmonious because all is yin and yang in constant undulating rhythms of advance or retreat, expansion or contraction, passivity or activity. The resultant absorption of one with the other add strength to all life, and results in the harmonious movement results of chi, or life force.

Thus, the moon and winter were ascribed to yin, and the more forceful sun and summer, to yang. Winter can be seen in color as the cooler shades of white, blue, and green, while the summer colors of yellow and red predominate as summer colors when the sun shines more brightly and warmly. Traditionally, women are associated with the moon and winter, and men with the sun and summer. These are in keeping with the Native American designations for men and women mentioned previously.

Fritjof Capra, author of *The Turning Point*, ascribes the following characteristics to yin and yang.

- **Yin:** feminine, contractive, conservative, responsive, cooperative, intuitive, and synthesizing
- **Yang:** masculine, expansive, demanding, aggressive, competitive, rational, and analytic

It is not difficult to concentrate on these yin and yang characteristics and see which colors they elicit in the mind's eye.

The moon and winter are easy to see in shades of pale greens and blues. Words like "feminine," "cooperative," and "intuitive," also bring these same colors to mind, with maybe a little yellow and light red thrown in for "conservative," "contractive," and "responsive."

The sun and summer belong to yang and instantly call forth strong reds and yellows. So might the words, "masculine," "demanding," and "aggressive." The words "expansive," "analytic," and "rational," might elicit a color response to orange—also a warm color.

Fortunately, in today's changing view of men and women, a person can choose the symbolic colors with which he or she wishes to be associated. Women are no longer simply considered the more passive gender, and men need not be linked to only an aggressive nature. Both men and women, in other words, can choose to be all colors.

Consider the following words and see what colors come to mind. If you do this exercise with someone else, the answers often will be similar.

- Dynamic
- Extrovert
- Introvert

- Subtle
- Instinctive
- Traditional
- Accepting
- Nourishing
- Gentle
- Demanding
- Aggressive
- Expansive
- Logical

OTHER CHARACTERISTICS
OF COLOR

The following personal characteristics are linked to certain colors in European-based symbolism, which permeates American culture. These symbolic colors are changing and will continue to change as the country becomes more ethnically diversified. The country as a whole will benefit and grow with these changes, and new color symbolism will slip into people's thinking without conscious awareness. The characteristics people now attribute to certain colors may someday be written about as "ancient" characteristics.

- **Black:** disciplined, strong willed, independent, opinionated
- **Blue (dark):** intelligent, strong, powerful, self-reliant
- **Blue (pale):** gentle, forgiving, lighthearted
- **Blue (greenish):** idealistic, faithful, sentimental, inventive, mature
- **Brown:** honest, supportive, structured, intellectual, active
- **Gold:** idealistic, noble, successful

- **Gray:** passive, noncommittal, stressed, burdened
- **Green (dark):** benevolent, humanistic, service-oriented, scientific, refreshing, cool, calm
- **Green (light):** innovative, adventuresome, self-motivated, desiring change
- **Lavender:** shy, indecisive, cautious
- **Light blue:** creative, perceptive, imaginative, analytic, youthful
- **Maroon:** sexual, emotional, sensitive
- **Mauve:** delicate, reserved, sensitive, encouraging
- **Mint green:** modest, insightful, composed, kind
- **Orange:** competent, flamboyant, sporting, active, organized, impatient
- **Purple:** instinctive, feeling, regal, spiritual
- **Peach:** gentle, charitable, enthusiastic
- **Pink (soft):** affectionate, compassionate, loving, sympathetic
- **Pink (bright):** action-oriented, sensual, assertive
- **Red (bright):** passionate, honest, ambitious, energetic, courageous, flamboyant, vital, extroverted
- **Red (deep or muted):** dignified, staunch, opinionated
- **Silver:** honest, trustworthy, romantic
- **Violet:** passionate, elegant, vibrant
- **White:** individualistic, egocentric, lonely, low self-esteem
- **Yellow (bright):** communicative, expressive, social
- **Yellow (pale):** low key, calm, natural

COLOR IDIOMS

The use of color to elicit certain responses or bring to mind particular images or feelings has given people a language unto itself.

Most of the terms associated with black have negative connotations, with the exception of "in the black," while pink is associated with happiness. White retains its clean, pure status, and yellow, as applied to Anglos, seems tainted with bias and prejudice. Red, of course, because it is an energetic color, is one of bravery and power. Blues and greens are mixed bags, and purple, through the ages has retained touches of its royal status by also referring to high emotion. Pink generally denotes optimism, except in the case of a pink slip, and had a negative connotation until the breakup of the Soviet bloc.

Black

- **Black Monday:** stock market crash of great Depression
- **Black mood:** depressed
- **Blackball:** ostracize
- **Blacklist:** list of censured individuals
- **Black book:** list of those ostracized
- **Blackmail:** extortion
- **Black mark:** derogatory sign on character
- **Black money:** unreported income
- **Blackout:** censorship
- **Black sheep:** family or group member in disgrace
- **Blacken:** tarnish a name
- **In the black:** debt free
- **Black hearted:** evil
- **Black magic:** negative use of spirituality
- **Blackleg:** strikebreaker or card cheat
- **Black art:** black magic
- **Black cats:** bad luck
- **Black is beautiful:** ethnic black pride
- **Black and blue:** sore
- **Black and white:** cop car, photos
- **Black death:** plague
- **Blackguard:** scoundrel

Blue

- **Blue:** feeling depressed
- **Blues:** soulful music
- **Blue Monday:** letdown after weekend
- **Blue moon:** seldom
- **Out of the blue:** unexpected
- **Blue blood:** aristocrat
- **Blue book:** list of socially prominent people
- **Blue chip:** stable stock
- **Blue collar:** industrial workers
- **True blue:** loyal
- **Blue (language):** risqué
- **Blue skies:** happy times
- **Blue laws:** puritanical
- **Out of the blue:** surprise
- **Bluenose:** uptight person
- **Blue-plate special:** inexpensive meal
- **Blue ribbon:** outstanding group
- **Blue stocking:** learned
- **Blue streak:** speedy

Gray

- **Gray area:** vague
- **Gray day:** a depressing day
- **Gray-haired:** old
- **Gray matter:** brains

Green

- **Folding green:** money
- **Greenbacks:** paper money
- **Green power:** economic power through money
- **Greenbelt:** reprieve from cement cities
- **Green horn:** inexperienced

- **Green thumb:** knack for growing plants
- **Green around the gills:** sickly
- **Green with envy:** very envious
- **Green-eyed:** jealous
- **Greener pastures:** more abundant or prosperous
- **Greening:** sensitive to human values
- **Green light:** go ahead
- **Green revolution:** improved agricultural techniques or environmental awareness

Pink
- **Tickled pink:** happy with results
- **Pink perfection:** tops
- **Pinko:** radical political views
- **Pink slip:** dismissal notice
- **Rose-colored glasses:** optimistic
- **In the pink:** good physical condition

Purple
- **Purple prose:** strong language
- **Purple with rage:** blind with rage
- **Born to purple:** high birth
- **Purple majesty:** purple mountain's majesty
- **Purple passion:** extreme emotion

Red
- **Red flag:** warning, symbol of revolution
- **In the red:** in debt
- **See red:** become angry
- **Red bait:** denounce with lack of evidence
- **Red-blooded:** hearty, strong-willed
- **Red carpet:** grand welcome
- **Red cent:** worthless

- **Red-handed:** caught in compromising position
- **Red herring:** ploy to divert attention from an issue
- **Red-hot:** new, current, excited
- **Red tape:** delays through bureaucracy
- **Red light district:** area of prostitution
- **Red-faced:** embarrassed
- **Red-letter days:** memorable times
- **Redneck:** derogatory term for working class conservative
- **Scarlet woman:** sinful

White

- **White:** pure
- **White with terror:** fearful
- **White magic:** non-evil intent
- **Bleed white:** to drain someone of money
- **White collar:** professional or clerical worker
- **White collar crime:** crimes of embezzlement or fraud
- **White elephant:** thing of limited value to owner
- **White feather:** sign of cowardice
- **White flag:** sign of surrender
- **White heat:** intense emotion
- **White hope:** a person expected to bring home honors
- **White lie:** trivial lie
- **White paper:** political propaganda
- **Wave a white flag:** surrender
- **Whitewash:** to cover up a deed
- **Lily white:** unsullied in a sarcastic way
- **White knight:** pure, and sometimes a savior

Yellow

- **Yellow:** coward
- **Yellow bellied:** coward
- **Yellow journalism:** sleazy reporting
- **Yellow peril:** fear of Eastern world political power

People continually add to their wealth of color symbolism, often on a personal level. Charles A. Reich's 1970 book, *The Greening of America*, spoke of a new consciousness opposing the commercial and social restrictions of the day. Green in the 1980s symbolized the addition of reverence for the earth, and all living things. During the Gulf War in one California community, a group of citizens went around their neighborhood placing yellow ribbons on several trees. Dana Brookins of Lytle Creek, California, ordered them to remove the yellow ribbon they had placed on her front-yard tree. She told them the ribbons should be red. She felt no joy about the war. To her it symbolized needless spilt blood.

CHAPTER 8

Color in Our Daily Living

Color specialists know that in addition to certain physiological and psychological responses to color that socioeconomic backgrounds, education, climate, place of birth, temperament, and other individual human characteristics, play a part in how individuals react to specific colors, even though people may be born with certain preferences.

This wasn't always the case, though. It wasn't until after the Renaissance that Europeans expanded their use of color as people know it today. Prior to that time, the use of color was dictated by mystics, philosophers, priests, and other holy men and women in a variety of cultures. Today, in some societies, such as Native Americans', a Holy Man will bestow on tribal members the colors one is to consider as his or her colors, especially for ceremonial use.

Additionally, until the fourteenth century in Europe, color was more practical and simple because fewer colors existed. They were derived from natural sources, and often their use was established for certain ritual functions, rather than as an important part of daily living.

Some non-European societies, though, made wide use of color, and to this day are more flamboyant than some European countries.

INDIVIDUAL COLOR PREFERENCES

Color preferences begin before people become conditioned to certain likes and dislikes in colors. Infants will stare longest at yellow, white, pink, and red. Young children prefer red and blue. The older individuals become, the more they prefer colors in the shorter wavelength such as blue and green.

The higher the income, the more complex a person's color choices become, such as preference for gray-greens instead of bright green; burgundy rather than red; and opaque rather than white. The less affluent may prefer brighter, simpler colors, according to marketing specialists who know how to tap these choices.

For eons, color choices were influenced by the location and habitat in which a person lived. People are more comfortable with the familiar. The colors surrounding the person's life—the desert, as opposed to a jungle, or a coastal community rather than a mountainous one—influence a person's color perceptions. The colors in a sunset may appear different when observed looking toward the Pacific Ocean rather than across a vast desert.

Also, the availability of certain natural dyes from plants and animals in the area where one lived affected choices in color.

All that is changing, though, as the world shrinks and cultures are influenced by one another. Also, the availability of a multitude of dyes makes change inevitable. For instance, a Public Broadcasting special on television concerning dance culture in different societies explains that some of the dances originated hundreds, and even thousands, of years ago.

The colors of the costumes worn by the performers were so beautiful and striking that I became more interested in the colors than the performances. I related my experience to color specialist Carlton Wagner, director of the Wagner Institute for Color Research in Santa Barbara.

He chuckled and said that most of the colors used today in the cultural costumes are not authentic, even though the dances may be. The natural dyes used before the advent of chemical dyes, were never so bright, and faded fast. So the costumes we see today are far more splendidly colored than at any time in history.

We have grown accustomed to a variety of vibrant colors, and make our selections among them.

PAINTS AND DYES

The earliest paints and dyes were made from natural sources. Most are now produced synthetically. Listed are but a few examples of natural dye sources from throughout the world.

- Lapis lazuli, a gemstone, was pulverized for a purple/blue.
- The cochineal insect provided red.
- Sulfur (sulphur) found in some soils provided a greenish-yellow.
- Seashells produced purple.
- Murex, a flesh-eating snail, provided purple dye.
- Iron clays produced brown.
- Chalk and lime produced white.

- Ochre, an iron oxide found in clay, produced red and yellow.
- Burnt bones and ivory provided black.
- A variety of berries were used for reds and blues.

In the nineteenth century Henry Perkins discovered what are called aniline dyes, derived from coal tar and carbon compounds. Modern chemistry now arranges thousands of complex carbon compounds creating a multitude of pigmented colors. These aniline dyes changed forever the concept of color in everything people use, and especially in the arts.

COLOR AND ART

The Impressionist painters of the nineteenth century were instrumental in changing the view of color in art. Many painted the same scene at different times of day illustrating the effect of the changing atmosphere. Pale glows of sunrise, the rose and mauves and gold of mid-day, and the final red-orange of sunset could change the perception of a single view, as demonstrated by Claude Monet's twenty-six depictions of the Rouen Cathedral in London, dated 1894, and painted at different times of the day. The atmospheric and climatic changes not only altered the canvas, but changed the feeling the picture elicited from the viewer.

Late nineteenth and early twentieth centuries expressionist artists such as Vincent Van Gogh and Paul Gauguin rejected the color schemes of the impressionists as lacking freedom because they used realistic colors. That is, the impressionists painted the colors represented by what they saw.

Van Gogh, among others, rejected this style and painted to express himself, or to show emotion. The seventh edition of

Gardner's *Art through the Ages* describes Van Gogh's "The Night Cafe" as conveying an oppressive atmosphere of evil by use of distortion of color. It is supposed to be felt rather than simply observed. The people depicted are a melancholy green. The ceiling, a poisonous green. The halos of light are yellow bad-smelling gases. The floor is an acid yellow, and the red walls, a feverish red.

So through the eyes of artists society is shown these subtle changes in light as depicted by the impressionists, and the emotions and feelings of an artist like Van Gogh. Viewers see and feel what the colors are trying to evoke because they elicit an emotional response. Sometimes that response is negative.

Valorie Hood, a computer consultant, provides a good example of how color in art affects people on an everyday level. On her second day at work on a project for Bank of America requiring about twelve hours a day of very intense work, the team she was working with met in the project room. At the same time, some new art works were being introduced at the corporate headquarters where she was stationed. Two pictures done in gray and black were hung on the walls of the project room. "Two huge pictures done in black and white with a hole in the center. We looked at them and it was a depressing sight after a day's work. Someone remarked that it reminded them of death. Another said it looked like the big, black hole they were ready to dive into." Such is the effect of color and design on the human psyche.

Location, too, plays on a person's like or dislike of certain painting. Barbara Cunningham, a Big Bear City, California, artist has noted on travels throughout the country that darker-toned paintings are more popular in the Eastern states where sunlight isn't as abundant as it is in the West. Thus, people in Western, or Sunbelt, states rely on lighter, and often more vibrant colors because the lighting surrounding their world is stronger and more vivid.

Bright primary colors give stronger energy than cooler colors such as pastels. Red and yellow are known as warm colors. To an artist, warm colors are seen as advancing colors. Cool colors, such as blue and green, are receding colors. White reflects light. Black absorbs it.

COLORING THE TIMES

The mood and temper of a society at any given time often dictate color preferences. Those who study the effects of color, such as color specialist Carlton Wagner, say the historical context of a society determines, in part, which colors will be popular during a particular era.

In 1992, during "Desert Storm," women in the United States began buying the colors seen in camouflaged suits to wear to work. They embraced the muted colors because the country, for the most part, was behind the war, according to Wagner.

Vietnam brought a different reaction. There was no color shift brought about because of empathy with the war because it remained controversial.

The 1960s, though, did bring changes in color consciousness. "The 1960s were rebellious and the youth wore colors that we normally don't put together, such as oranges with purple, or with red. Yellow with lime," says Wagner. Hot pink and bright orange were popular colors not only because of Vietnam, but due to the agitated state brought about by the rise of feminism, and the attitude of open sexuality. Ironically, orange clothing is known to attract hostility.

Art historians studying dress preceding the French Revolution liken it to the colors and fashions used by the "flower children" of the late 1960s.

Blue jeans also became popular when American youth were

concerned about the Vietnam conflict. It may have expressed a need for security and desire for more group representation.

The 1970s heralded a decade of earth tones as the Vietnam war wound down. But the colors were muted because of the threat of nuclear war. The nation felt powerless, and earth tones seemed safe.

The 1980s brought a more optimistic color palette, and may have expressed the public's desire for more artistic creativity. The neutral colors of gray became popular, and muted, pastels and other safe colors, took over.

Today, somewhat similar to the 1960s, the mood is toward harmony and peace, and blue jeans remain popular. Yet, if the government sends fighting troops to any of the hot spots in the world today, and if the American public gets behind it, Americans will see a shift in color preferences, according to Wagner. At present, the colors of choice are associated with the earth because of the environmental movement. But if the country goes to war, the colors will shift, he says.

Also, if the country continues to be in an economically depressed state, colors may also shift. During times of economic stress light blues, grays, blacks, and brown are popular. Black has already entered the mainstream in clothing.

CULTURAL DIVERSITY

English-speaking people have certain words that stand for particular colors—vermillion, aqua, hot-pink and so forth. People see these colors, and use certain words to convey the thoughts of what they have seen.

Not all cultures have the same boundaries or words for color categories. Morton Hunt, in *The Universe Within*, says the Dani of New Guinea have only two terms for color— "mili" for "dark," and "mola" for "light."

Hunt points out, though, that the Dani think about and see the variety of existing colors much the same way as someone from another culture. They simply don't have the same words to convey their thoughts.

David Crystal, compiler of *The Cambridge Encyclopedia of Language* says the English language contains eleven basic color stems or units: white, black, red, green, yellow, blue, brown, purple, pink, orange, and gray. Other cultures, like the Dani, might have two, or more, but the greatest number is eleven. Also, a single word can convey different color meanings, depending on what object it is used. Thus, the Japanese word "awo" can mean green, blue, or pale, depending on whether it refers to such things as vegetables, the ocean, or clouds.

CULTURAL COLOR ASSOCIATIONS

Ethnic groups appear to have color preferences. These preferences are conditioned by the climate and terrain from the country of origination, and even from the area within that country. These preferences originated because they were the colors common to the area. For example, different parts of the country in the United States once utilized colors specific to the area. Various shades of green and brown may have predominated in Vermont, while yellows, oranges, and pastels were more popular in Arizona.

Vegetation native to the area also played an important role in the colors of choice. People who lived in more tropical areas had access to more vegetable dyes simply because the vegetation was more abundant and diverse. These dyes were used for clothing and decorating.

For instance, the Spanish and South Americans come from cultures that use bright colors. All the burial vaults are painted in bright, fantastic colors, and the clothing is bright because they had access to a multitude of natural bright dyes, according to psychology professor Stanley Coren.

Coren points out that the buildings in Greece, such as the Acropolis, were originally painted bright colors. "We think of these buildings in whites and grays, but they were originally painted bright colors. It would be shocking to us to see the Venus de Milo painted a flesh tone, but that's how she was originally done," he says.

People in Northern Europe didn't have access to the variety of dyes available in Southern Europe, such as Greece. Plus, Northern Europeans were far more monastic and restrained than their counterparts to the South.

Also at work is a cultural response. "We find that the effects of color on people is really in many respects culturally determined. Individuals who grew up around dark, earth colors feel fairly secure with these colors in their surroundings," says Coren.

The response to color in a person's surroundings probably was much stronger when men and women lived closer to nature, but is being revitalized today with the environmental movement.

The color preferences of people in the United States, though, is changing due to the accessibility of a multitude of dyes that produce bright colors. Also, they are being influenced by an influx of cultures that are comfortable with much brighter colors than those traditionally used by Europeans.

It is a multicultural society, and increasingly, people of all races and classes are embracing the colors of different societies.

"If you take individuals growing up today, the culture is such that they are familiar with brighter, warmer colors. For example, the kids who come into my classes wear clothes in colors my generation would have considered a gag. These brighter colors are a comfort, though, to this generation," says Coren.

"Bright colors were associated with frivolity, and that was taboo in Northern Europe," says Coren. Also vegetable dyes in Northern Europe, which would have provided some of the brighter colors, washed off too easily. Those produced from minerals were longer lasting and more widely used, but they produced the more subdued colors.

Royalty were usually first to obtain new colors, such as purple, because they were the only ones who could afford it, since the dye for the color had to be imported.

Thus, the availability of color, as well as the prevailing social attitude, dominates a culture's color choices. "In Japanese culture red and pink are considered festive colors. If you have a festive occasion you will wrap gifts in red or pink," says Coren. "Yet, red is not a festive color in North African societies where it is associated with violence. It is seldom used except during war time, and then a red sash is used to indicate that the person is going to war." Studies show that in the United States red is also popular during war time.

Other research has shown that American Indians prefer red, blue, violet, green, orange, and yellow. Filipinos prefer red, green, blue, violet, orange, and yellow. Blacks prefer blue, red, green, violet, orange, and yellow.

DESIGN AND ADVERTISING

Patricia Verlodt, a color consultant who heads Color Services in Hanover Park, Illinois, specializing in industrial consumer products, says that when products are equal in value and quality, color is the number one reason that nudges a person into making a selection.

Colors literally dominate a person's choices in foods, clothes, decorating, housewares, landscaping, and adornments.

To further understand the importance of color in advertising, all one has to do is note that condoms now come in colors. But specific colors are employed by manufacturers, advertisers, clothing designers, and the work force to get you to buy the products, and to elicit certain responses.

For example, fast food places use orange because it is a high-energy color and appetite stimulant. It encourages "eat and run." But orange has come to also denote cheapness. Red is a universal sign of danger and is used to get an immediate response. It is the longest ray in the visible spectrum and makes a greater impression on the retina. It also speeds up the emotions.

Yellow, though, is more stimulating than red, so yellow flyers are used extensively in advertising. It's easy to overdose on yellow, though, and too much can make a person angry and hostile. Also, some people have an aversion to yellow accompanied by black because it reminds them of insects.

Green, in the middle of the spectrum, is calming and balancing, and for years was used in hospital rooms. Today, green is in because of the environmental movement. Green also makes people feel secure. It is popular on everything from the eyes, as eye shadow, to wedding gowns where green silk leaves as trim have become popular. Hunter green, a dark, woodsy green has become a popular color of jeans for women. A certain shade of green, though, such as one with lots of yellow in it that has come to be known as "bilious green," can literally make people sick.

But much more is at work when manufacturers select a particular color to emphasize, and get consumers to buy their products. Some nuances of color choice are far more subtle than grabbing a person's attention. A manufacturer may want to elicit a sense of calm, establish credibility, or pique a person's sense of responsibility. For example, the 1990s use of "clear" products pushes the message that the product is somehow more environmentally superior or pure.

"It's no secret that clear is a knee-jerk reaction to the environment. People think there are no chemicals in it, and that it won't pollute. The only difference is there are no dyes in it, but it has just as many chemicals," says Verlodt.

"Clear" also gives the impression that honesty and integrity is back in vogue, as opposed to "coloring" the truth, says Verlodt.

Some of the major soft drink bottling companies now produce the traditional brown colas as clear, and coffee is now available in clear colors. Carlton Wagner says no studies have been done on why "clear" is in right now, but that part of the reason may be that consumers have been saturated with color and are looking for an alternative.

Another reason for the popularity of "clear" may be that some people are tired of having to make so many decisions and a noncolor lets them off the hook for a while. "It eliminates having to make a decision. Clear goes with everything," says Wagner.

Wagner, who has directed color choices for the likes of General Motors, Mercedes Benz, Sears Roebuck and Company, Ace Hardware, Ford Motor Company and U.S. Gypsum, says there is always a shifting of what one considers ideal, and that color in our personal lives goes from one area to another.

People have an idea in mind—a fantasy—when they begin looking for something, such as an ideal car, and they have a preconceived idea of what they want. "A company can't introduce a color that the public isn't ready for," says Wagner. Yellow as a color for cars hasn't been popular since the 1940s and early 1950s. A company would be sticking its neck out to introduce a yellow car right now, unless it suddenly became popular because of some association, such as with a popular sports figure.

So clear and green will be with consumers in the 1990s because they sell. Within a few years, the color trends can change.

Another new "in" color for the 1990s is purple. As with the clear and green phenomenon, purple also carries the tones of a society's changing values.

"You either love purple or you hate it," says Verlodt. But it is loved now more than at any time in history because of the feminist movement. Color is becoming unisex. "Males are accepting more color now. They have become more open-minded—the younger generation especially," says Verlodt. "The rules that once applied no longer do. It's exciting to break the rules of tradition."

Purple, especially gray-purple, is now a popular color for cars. At the same time, cars are becoming more rounded—another sign of the feminist movement, according to Verlodt.

As certain colors become popular, others go out of fashion. At one time yellow and blue together were viewed as elegant colors. Now they are considered tacky and cheap. Because the combination was so popular it may have been overused until it became too common. The same may happen with green, purple, and clear.

Colors, so to speak, have their day in the sun.

ARCHITECTURE AND DESIGN

A mystical relationship has always existed between color and architecture. Egyptian buildings often had green floors like the meadows of the Nile, and many ancient temples had blue ceilings like the sky.

When it comes to color in architecture and design, people in the United States tend to be stuffy. Verlodt, who consults with house paint manufacturers throughout the world, says that in countries such as New Zealand and Australia bright colors Americans would never think of using are common.

"We're chicken. We're afraid someone is going to say we're different. So we stick with earth tones. It is safe. It's not unusual to see hot pink roofs in New Zealand," Verlodt says. "Their roofs are metal, and they paint them any color they desire. So the houses are more colorful. It's a good climate with lots of tropical flowers, and the people are energetic," she says. Their brightly painted houses reflect that energy.

The Chinese belief in *feng shui* that links the directional placement of certain objects to fate, calls for black objects placed on the north side of a room to attract prosperity. White is disdained in the home since the Chinese link it with mourning. Plum colors attract respect, and purple and deep red in the home draw power.

But as with clothing, Americans are becoming more willing to take chances with color in architecture, both at work and in the home, partly due to the changing attitude about the work environment that calls for a more open and natural work setting.

This change in attitude has developed for many reasons, chief among them is the amount of time workers spend in offices devoid of natural stimulation. As a reporter, I once worked in a large newsroom where no natural light entered the building. At certain times of the year, I drove to work before the sun was up, and left after the sun went down. Other staff, as well as myself, felt the deprivation.

Designers and planners now know that such deprivation can lead to physiological and psychological illnesses, resulting not only in less production, but unhappy workers.

This same knowledge has spilled over into the design of hospitals, convalescent homes, and to any structure where people spend a great deal of time.

At the same time, the Western world is becoming more open to a multitude of new colors that are richer, more saturated, and vibrant than ever before. Decorators are urging customers to be more bold in color selections, and mixing colors that were once believed not to match. Tricia Guild, founder of London's Designers Guild, and author of *Tricia Guild on Color*, says that color in the home has a profound impact on people's lives. It can uplift a person, and inspire the senses.

The colors used in decorating can also elicit certain psychological and emotional responses according to many studies. Some of these responses are determined by modern technology. Before the advent of insulation, and windows constructed and designed to keep out the cold, houses usually contained small windows, because large ones would have let in too much cold or heat. Today, though, due to new technology, people are demanding more and larger windows, skylights, and pocket doors that let in the light. They recognize the value of more natural light in their lives, and also want a sense of openness within their homes. With more light, colors become ever more dominant.

In 1973 *Time* ran an article on research in Munich, Germany, that showed rooms painted light blue, yellow, yellow-green, and orange could raise IQs as much as twelve points, whereas, white, black, and brown rooms caused a drop in IQ. It was also found that orange raised the spirits and lessened hostility and irritability.

The above are basic colors, and elicit profound responses. But all color, even subtle shades in some way, create particular atmospheres that directly affect people.

THE COLOR OF FOOD

I attended a St. Patrick's Day banquet where green dye had been added to the butter, turning it a yellow/green shade. No one touched it. Rolls were eaten *sans* butter.

This shouldn't be so surprising. A yellow-green shade is one that turns people off. Other colors that make people food shy are gray, blue, black, and purple. Try a blue light in the refrigerator to reduce the appetite.

Black is associated with decay, and gray reminds people of something old. Blue is perceived as moldy, although it is acceptable in blue cheese.

Orange is considered an appetite stimulant. Orange, along with red, yellow, and some shades of brown, affects the autonomic nervous system thus stimulating the appetite. Just ask a chocoholic.

Red touches in foods enhance their appeal. Even if a person doesn't like red cherries, adding them to a dish tricks the mind into believing the food tastes better. And a variety of different colored foods on a plate is more appetizing than food of the same color.

Cultural color preferences also play a role in food appeal. "Pink is one of the most popular colors in Japan, so Pacific salmon became popular there because of its pink color," says Stanley Coren.

COLOR AND CLOTHING

By the 1970s, all the old rules of color in clothing began breaking apart. It followed on the heels of racial desegregation, free speech and feminist movements, gay rights advocacy, and New Age philosophies.

The color spectrum had found a new voice. Grandmothers were no longer relegated to gray, black, and maroon. The tan or gray cardigan sweater is no longer the domain of men past fifty. Large size women no longer had to sport around in dark colors that supposedly made them look thinner.

Little girls stopped wearing ruffled pastels. Red outfits on women didn't signal hooker status. Boy babies didn't have to wear blue and girls pink. Black had long been associated with older women. All that changed, along with many other color traditions. Up until the 1950s, wearing contrasting colors such as pink and red together, was taboo. No longer. Contrasting colors are found in all fashion wear.

Black has universally been the most popular choice for workout clothes, mostly because it makes people look thinner since dark colors recede. But by the 1980s, a rainbow of colored workout clothes started making their appearance in the nation's gyms. Today, gyms are virtually laced with colors.

A gym instructor from Jack LaLanne's told me that the change came about because people began feeling better about their bodies. "When they first come in they're usually in the traditional black, but after their bodies get in better shape, they start wearing brighter colors," he says. Black, though, also suggests sophistication, with an undertone of danger or evil. So it will always be popular in one form or another.

Today people walk about in a splash of colors, although most have favorites. What a person feels good in, he or she usually looks best in. Looks are in great part determined by how a person feels from the inside out.

The popular poem, "When I Am an Old Woman I Shall Wear Purple," recounted in a book by the same name, emphasizes this point by saying, "When I am an old woman I shall wear purple with a red hat which doesn't go, and doesn't suit me."

Tradition, too, held that large-bodied people should wear solid, dark colors. Today the fashion industry is conscious that everyone isn't a size five, and they are designing colorful, bright, clothing for all sizes. The backlash against the clothing industry, and against the bias and stereotyping of large-sized women, was precipitated by activists and the introduction of several magazines dedicated to the beauty of large-bodied women.

Jane Milstead, editor at *Big Beautiful Woman*, grew up with all the hang-ups of a large-sized woman in American society. She recalls how early experiences with clothes taught her that she was doomed to wear black dresses with a rose on the shoulder that had to be removed, or "flowered tops from hell."

"Then I discovered I looked pretty in pink," she says.

"Women still think they have to be thin to get a man to love them, but it begins with how you feel from within."

With the nudging from magazines like *Big Beautiful Woman*, most of the major clothes designers and manufacturers finally got the message—part of which was that they were out of touch with a good portion of the buying public—and today, large-bodied women can dress as stylishly and flamboyantly as anyone.

"They began to realize we were a market to reckon with. That we were just like other women and were out there doing all sorts of things with our lives," she says. "We know now that diets don't work, that people can be larger and healthy, and that we don't need the media telling us how we should look. Individuality can get lost in the media hype."

COLOR FADS IN CLOTHING

Despite individual preferences for colors, though, Americans are influenced daily to try colors they may not have ever considered.

These influences come from television, the theater, in the marketplace, by newsmakers, and a person's own changing sense of self.

The television program "Evening Shade," helped make green popular, according to Wagner. The popularity of pastels in the late 1980s has also been attributed to the television program "Miami Vice." Men who would never have been caught dead in pinks and lavenders suddenly embraced those colors.

Pam Johnson's lavender kitchen in "My Sister Sam" influenced the use of lavender in the home. Barbara Bush was responsible for lots of blue in clothing choices. Blue suggests loyalty and sincerity. "They have to like what they see in the person in order to make the color popular," says Wagner. "If Princess Di appears in certain colors, they start selling."

Warm browns and tans suggest stability, security, and domestic comfort. It is also associated with the earth and nature, and takes its place with green as popularly associated with the environmental movement. Since it is commonly linked to the earth, it is associated with the mid-1990s movement toward a simpler, and more traditional way of life.

Drab browns or faded greens may relate to obedience and conformity, or green could suggest freedom. To wear green connects humans with the powers of nature. People often think of Ireland as the "Emerald Isle," because of the green lushness of that country.

Red stands for vitality and life.

Traditionally purple clothing was associated with royalty, chiefly because it required dye from a rare and expensive type of shellfish. The masses couldn't afford it until the advent of aniline dye in the nineteenth century. Then it became one of the most popular of colors until it was overdone and became likened to tawdriness. Rejuvenated after World War II, it was the forerunner of many variations, including lavender, lilac, and plum, that are still popular clothing colors today.

Pink clothing is romantic and sentimental, although Oscar Wilde, nineteenth century author and satirist, had other ideas. He said, "Never trust a woman who wears mauve or a woman over thirty-five who is fond of pink ribbons. It means they have a history."

SEASONAL TYPECASTING

In the 1970s, a color consciousness in clothes developed around the theme of linking a person's seasonal type to the colors he or she should wear. Thus, an autumnal type person would look best in oranges, browns, and gold. A spring type had preferences for pastels, a summer person should eschew warm bright colors, and a winter individual would naturally prefer whites, grays, blues, and blacks.

Autumn types have skin that is ivory, peach, coppery, or golden brown or beige. Their hair reflects shades of red, off-white or blond, and muted shades of brown or black. Eyes can be dark or golden brown, hazel, green flecked, gray/blue, or bright turquoise.

A winter person tends to have white or light/gray or rosy beige skin, olive or dark skin with a blue undertone. The hair is dark brown or auburn, blue-black, white, or salt and pepper. The eyes are reddish or black-brown, hazel, gray/blue or dark blue, or gray/green.

Spring individuals are associated with cream or ivory-toned skin, sometimes with freckles; peach, pink, or golden beige skin. Cheeks are often rosy. The hair can be honey, strawberry, or yellow blond; auburn, yellow/brown, light gray, or off-white. Clear blues and greens are their eye colors, sometimes with white or golden flecks in them. Aqua eyes also belong to the spring group.

Summer people have complexions ranging from pale to rosy beige, and rosy to gray/browns. Hair tends toward blond shades of white, ash, dark yellow, to browns of all shades, and grays with blue and pearl white tints. The eyes can be cloudy blue or green, or extremely clear blues, aquas, or hazel.

Most people, though, have an instinctive sense about what colors look good on them. If a person is comfortable in a particular color, his or her chances of looking good in it are increased. Many people pay too much attention to the color preferences of others—spouses, salespeople, and what is touted as hot in magazines, when, in reality, they are the best judge of what colors to wear.

A friend of Milstead's, whom she says "follows every fad," had her personal colors analyzed and came away wearing mauve. "She looked like she had been dead for a week," says Milstead. A growing number of people would agree with Milstead's view about color coordinating. That is, individuals might want to consider wearing the colors that make them feel good, that establish their moods, or that they just plain like, without having to worry about whether it's the "proper" color for them. There's more at work when a person selects colors than what matches the complexion or eyes. Color in clothing can be more fun when one uses the imagination, the spark of intuition, and personal feelings.

PERSONAL GROOMING

Makeup fads come and go, but one of the major changes in the 1990s has been the demise of the tan, due to reports of how the sun damages the skin. Many Anglos have come to envy the natural dark beige and tan faces of their black and Latino counterparts.

People are becoming bolder in the use of makeup colors with brighter and deeper lipsticks and rouges, although certain segments of the population disdain any makeup at all—a link to the environmental movement that calls for the natural look. Brighter dyes are in for the hair, too, with reds being a color of choice. It's not only women, anymore, who are affected. Male rock stars began the revolution with bright fuchsia and orange hair. They have gone on to a variety of shades of green to canary yellow and turquoise. Its roots go back to the punk movement of the 1970s.

HOW TO ELICIT CERTAIN RESPONSES WITH COLOR

In addition to following the dictates of moods and likes and dislikes in clothing color, a person may have other motivations.

A noted metaphysical counselor and one-time Hollywood costume designer discussed the effect of colors when one is trying to make a certain impression or elicit a particular response from someone else.

He offered the following tips:

- **Communication:** Yellow is a friendly color, associated with cheerfulness and hope. It creates enthusiasm and immediately it says, "I want to communicate." Yellow is good when visiting a sick friend, but not one undergoing anxiety because too much yellow can add to the anxiety. Pink is also a color of communication. Like yellow, it is a color of vitality. Bright yellow is known to increase the heartbeat, while pink is associated with love and affection.
- **Concealing emotion:** If one is going to meet one's partner's parents, impress them with neatness and beige tones of clothing, which are warm, but not too aggressive. Wearing beige is a color that helps you to conceal emotions.
- **Overcoming depression:** Bright, aggressive colors release energy when one is feeling sluggish. If a

person is depressed, wearing a bright color may help him or her when dealing with others, even though it seems difficult to do so.

- **Asserting oneself:** Red stands for strength and aggression, and can also denote passion and anger. Red, being the color of blood, prepares a person for physical action. Some people literally "see red" when faced with that color. It increases blood pressure and heart rates.

- **Appearing calm:** Blue portrays humility and gentleness. It has a calming effect and can even reduce blood pressure. It is a restful color. The lighter the blue, the less threatening the wearer will appear to others. Whenever one wants to appear innocent, one should wear light blues.

- **Generating respect:** Dark blues add importance to people. They are perceived as hardworking and serious. Blue shades also generate sympathy. But it's most formidable use is to generate respect. If a person is testifying in court, navy blue is a good color to wear. It says, "I'm telling the truth."

- **Promoting authority:** Black gives authority and emphasizes drama. If a person is going to "lay down the law," he or she should wear black. Black can make the conversation serious. It suggest religious piety, but can also be sophisticated or sexually suggestive in certain clothing.

- **Displaying passion:** Mauve-pinks and purples show passion. Purple is more aggressive than pink. Lavender is great for attracting the opposite sex because it sends the signal that the person can be manipulated.

- **Displaying royalty or vulgarity:** Dark purples,

although associated with royalty, can give the impression of vulgarity when worn for everyday wear. They are not good colors to use when trying to make an impression.

- **Creating ambivalence:** One of the most dangerous colors, however, is magenta, a mixture of blue and red. Red excites and blue depresses, so it creates ambivalence.
- **Being nurturing and open:** To show a nurturing nature, wear brown, the warm earth color. If a person wants to indicate responsibility, brown is again the color to wear since it sends a message of informality and openness.
- **Diffusing a situation:** If a person is entering into a volatile situation, he or she should wear green. It creates an atmosphere of peace. Green can reduce stress, and may be why people head to the mountains for renewal. It also creates a sense of security.
- **Appearing indefinite:** Gray makes an indefinite statement. Someone who wears gray doesn't want to be noticed. Gray creates no strain on the eye. So if a person wants to slip in and out unseen, gray is a good color to wear. Gray, though, inspires creativity, and promotes an appreciation of the arts.
- **Making a statement:** Contrasting shades of light and dark, especially black and white, make a statement. People will pay attention to a person wearing these colors.
- **Showing competency:** White creates an atmosphere of competency, goodness, and trustworthiness. Doctors, nurses, and dentists give an example of how white engenders trust.

The person's personality also enters into the picture. If he or she is an outgoing, aggressive type, he or she may feel some discomfort wearing pale shades. And if the person is an introvert, bright colors may not be the best choice. Others will pick up this uneasiness, so when selecting colors, a person should choose shades that make him or her feel good about the choice.

COLOR AS A UNIVERSAL LANGUAGE

Certain colors have become universal in many parts of the world, and represent a common language. In the United States these colors were adopted by Congress and the Occupational Safety and Health Administration in 1970. Some are standard in other Western countries.

- **Red:** Fire protection, such as alarm boxes, extinguishers, hydrants and hose connections, sprinkler lines and, of course, fire-fighting equipment.
- **Orange:** Warning for acute hazards, such as near hazardous tools or equipment, exposed electric wires and hazardous machinery.
- **Yellow and black bands:** Road equipment, such as cranes and backhoes, and to mark railings around hazardous areas.
- **Blue:** For marking equipment that needs permission to operate such as generators or welding gear.
- **Green:** The color of medicine is used on first aid boxes, on cabinets, and for gas masks.

The use of color in people's surroundings at work, at play, in the home, in dress, and even shade of hair, profoundly affects them throughout the day. People even select their foods partly based on color. Choices are seldom arbitrary. They have deeply rooted meanings, and can color a day bright or gloomy. People have choice in their selections, usually to a greater extent than many of the other forces they encounter in their lives. It can be a rainbow of choice when old stereotypes are shed, and come alive to the available abundance of color.

BIBLIOGRAPHY

Birren, Faber. *Color and Human Response*. New York: Van Nostrand Reinhold Co., 1978.

Brennan, Barbara Ann. *Hands of Light*. New York: Bantam, 1987.

Brown, Barbara B. *New Mind, New Body*. New York: Harper & Row, 1974.

Capra, Fritjof. *The Turning Point*. New York: Simon and Schuster, Inc., 1982.

Capra, Fritjof. *The Tao of Physics*. New York: Simon and Schuster, Inc., 1975.

Cayce, Edgar. *Auras*. Virginia Beach, VA: A.R.E. Press, 1945.

Crystal, David. *The Cambridge Encyclopedia of Language*. Cambridge, NY: Cambridge University Press, 1987.

Dewey, John. *Art As Experience*. New York: Capricorn Books, G. P. Putnam's Sons, 1958.

Eiseman, Leatrice. *Alive with Color*. Washington, D.C.: Acropolis Books Ltd., 1983.

Frankl, Viktor E. *Man's Search for Meaning*. New York: Simon and Schuster, Inc., 1984. Originally published in Austria in 1946 under the title *Ein Psycholog erlebt das Konzentrationslager*, and translated by Beacon Press in 1959.

Gauquelin, Michael. *How Cosmic and Atmospheric Energies Affect Your Health*. New Mexico: Aurora, 1984.

Harding, M. Ester. *Woman's Mysteries*. New York: Bantam Books Inc., 1973.

Hunt, Morton. *The Universe Within*. New York: Simon and Schuster, 1982.

Hunt, Roland. *Lighting Therapy and Color Harmony*. London: C. W. Daniel Co., Ltd., 1950.

Kieffer, Gene [ed.]. *Kundalini for the New Age*. New York: Bantam, 1988.

Lee, Lawrence. *An Appreciation of Stained Glass*. New York: Oxford University Press, 1977.

Lurie, Alison. *The Language of Clothes*. New York: Vintage House, a Division of Random House, 1981.

Luscher, Dr. Max. *The Lucher Color Test*: translated and edited by Ian Scott, based on the original German text by Dr. Max Luscher, New York: Pocket Books, 1969.

Mella, Dorothee L. *The Language of Color*. New York: Warner Communications Co., 1988.

McKenzie, Norman. *Dreams and Dreaming*. London: Aldus Books Limited, 1965.

Moss, Thelma. *The Body Electric*. Los Angeles: J. P. Tarcher, Inc., 1979.

Nichols, Sallie. *Jung and Tarot: An Archetypal Journey*. York Beach, ME: Samuel Weiser Inc., 1980.

Restak, Richard, M.D. *The Brain*. New York: Bantam Books, 1984.

Slater, Paula B., and Sinor, Barbara. *Beyond Words*. Middletown, CA: Harbin Springs Publishing, 1990.

Sun, Howard and Dorothy. *Color Your Life*. New York: Ballantine Books, 1993.

Wall, Vicky. *The Miracle of Colour Healing*. London: The Aquarian Press, 1990.

Watson, Lyall. *Lightning Bird*. New York: Simon and Schuster, 1982.

White, John, and Krippner, S. *Future Science*. New York: Anchor Books, 1977.

Wolf, Fred Alan. *Star Wave: Mind, Consciousness, and Quantum Physics*. New York: Macmillan Publishing Co., 1984.